I'll Never Know What Made Me Do It

YOU KNOW WHAT IT'S LIKE WHEN YOU SEE A SKIRT OR A PAIR OF JEANS YOU REALLY WANT AND JUST MUST HAVE? USUALLY YOU CAN HELP MUM AROUND THE HOUSE WITH A COUPLE OF THINGS AND SHE'LL GIVE IN TO YOU. OR IF THAT DOESN'T WORK, THERE'S ALWAYS DAD. BUT IT WASN'T AS EASY AS THAT FOR CATHY. Y'SEE, CATHY'S MUM WAS DIVORCED AND THERE WAS HARDLY EVER ANY SPARE CASH FOR EXTRAS.

THAT FANTASTIC SKIRT'S STILL THERE. I THOUGHT SOMEONE WOULD'VE BOUGHT IT AGES AGO. IT'S NOT DEAR, EITHER, BUT I COULDN'T AFFORD IT EVEN IF IT WAS HALF THAT PRICE.

TIM! OF COURSE I REMEMBER YOU.

HOW COULD I EVER FORGET! IT BROKE MY HEART WHEN YOU LEFT HERE TO GO TO COLLEGE.

MAYBE I COULD GO AND TRY IT ON, JUST TO SEE IF IT WOULD FIT. BUT THAT MIGHT BE ASKING FOR TROUBLE. I MIGHT BE TEMPTED TO DO SOMETHING SILLY—LIKE WALKING OUT OF THE SHOP WITH IT!

HEY, IT'S CATHY PRICE, ISN'T IT? REMEMBER ME—TIM GREY?

HOW'RE YOU GETTING ON, THEN? IT MUST BE TWO YEARS SINCE I LAST SAW YOU.

I'VE LEFT SCHOOL BUT I HAVEN'T MANAGED TO GET A JOB—NOT YET.

HE'S STILL THE SAME— AND THAT SMILE OF HIS STILL MAKES MY HEART LEAP.

5

Y'KNOW, CATHY. I ALWAYS WANTED TO ASK YOU OUT, BUT YOU NEVER SEEMED ALL THAT INTERESTED IN BOYS.

I WAS PRETTY BUSY WITH HOMEWORK AND I HAD TO HELP MUM AROUND THE HOUSE.

IF ONLY HE KNEW—I COULDN'T GO ANYWHERE, 'COS I NEVER HAD ANYTHING DECENT TO WEAR!

LOOK, I'M HAVING A BIT OF PARTY ON SATURDAY— JUST SOME OF THE GANG I USED TO HANG AROUND WITH. HOW ABOUT COMING ALONG?

SATURDAY? OH, YES, I...OH, BUT WAIT A MINUTE, I'M NOT SURE I CAN MAKE IT, TIM. CAN I—ER—GIVE YOU A RING?

OK, BUT I HOPE YOU MANAGE TO MAKE IT. SEE YOU!

OH, WHY DID I SAY THAT? NOW HE'LL THINK I DON'T WANT TO GO TO HIS PARTY AND I DO—MORE THAN ANYTHING ELSE IN THE WORLD!

BUT ALL THE OTHER GIRLS WILL BE GETTING SOMETHING NEW. I JUST COULDN'T FACE THEM IN MY ANCIENT DRESS—YET AGAIN. IT'D BE DIFFERENT IF I HAD SOMETHING NICE TO WEAR—LIKE THAT SKIRT. BUT IT'S A WASTE OF TIME EVEN THINKING ABOUT IT. AND, ANYWAY, THIS WON'T GET OLD MRS STEVENS' SHOPPING DONE!

Mrs Stevens was confined to the house.

THANK YOU, DEAR. IT'S SO GOOD OF YOU TO GO FOR MY SHOPPING EVERY WEEK. I DON'T KNOW WHAT I'D DO WITHOUT YOU.

I ENJOY DOING IT. AND YOU'RE ALWAYS SO CHATTY, I LOOK FORWARD TO SEEING YOU.

HERE'S THE RECEIPT FOR THAT BILL YOU ASKED ME TO PAY. BEFORE I FORGET, YOU GAVE ME A POUND TOO MUCH.

DID I? DEAR ME, I NEVER NOTICED. I GET SO CONFUSED THESE DAYS. IT'S JUST AS WELL YOU'RE AN HONEST GIRL, CATHY.

D'YOU WANT ANYTHING ELSE BEFORE I GO, MRS STEVENS? YOUR GLASSES ARE UP HERE ON THE MANTELPIECE.

PASS THEM DOWN, DEAR. MY HEAD FEELS A BIT FUZZY TODAY, SO I THINK I'LL JUST SIT QUIETLY AND READ THE PAPER.

But something else caught Cathy's eye . . .

GOOD HEAVENS, THERE MUST BE ABOUT TWENTY FIVERS HERE! MRS STEVENS REALLY SHOULDN'T KEEP ALL THIS MONEY IN THE HOUSE. BUT OLD PEOPLE ARE SOME-TIMES FUNNY ABOUT BANKS.

Suddenly another thought entered Cathy's head . . .

JUST TWO OF THESE WOULD BUY THAT SKIRT. I'M SURE MRS STEVENS WOULD NEVER MISS THEM. I BET SHE DOESN'T EVEN KNOW HOW MUCH IS HERE!

And so . . .

IT'S STILL THERE. THANK GOODNESS! I'LL PHONE TIM AND TELL HIM I'LL BE THERE ON SATURDAY. ANYWAY, I SHOULDN'T FEEL GUILTY. AFTER ALL, IT'S NOT AS IF I'M DOING SOMETHING REALLY WICKED—LIKE ROBBING SOMEBODY POOR. MRS STEVENS ALWAYS SAYS SHE HAS EVERYTHING SHE NEEDS.

BUT ALL THE ARGUMENTS RANG FALSE. DEEP IN HER HEART, CATHY KNEW THAT ONCE SHE SPENT THE MONEY, SHE'D BE A COMPLETELY DIFFERENT PERSON—SOMEBODY SHE'D FIND IT VERY HARD TO LIVE WITH!

So . . .

I MUST HAVE BEEN MAD! I'LL TAKE BACK THE SKIRT TOMORROW, THEN GO AND SEE MRS STEVENS. IF I TELL HER HOW SORRY I AM AND EXPLAIN WHY I DID IT, SHE'LL MAYBE FORGIVE ME. AT LEAST THEN I'LL BE ABLE TO LIVE WITH MYSELF, EVEN IF I NEVER DO HAVE NICE CLOTHES, OR A BOYFRIEND!

But next day . . .

NO ANSWER. THAT'S FUNNY. I KNOW MRS STEVENS CAN'T GO OUT BY HERSELF!

She met one of the neighbours.

ARE YOU LOOKING FOR MRS STEVENS, LOVE? I'M AFRAID THEY'VE TAKEN HER TO HOSPITAL. THE HOME HELP FOUND HER ON THE FLOOR THIS MORNING!

WHAT? OH, NO!

She dashed to the nearest phone box.

D- DIED IN THE AMBULANCE? YES, I- I UNDERSTAND . . . THANK YOU.

OH, NO! I CAN'T BELIEVE IT!

ARE YOU A RELATIVE?

N- NO, J- JUST A FRIEND. PLEASE, WHICH HOSPITAL IS SHE IN? I'VE GOT TO KNOW HOW SHE IS!

Cathy walked away stunned, and . . .

HEY, WHAT ABOUT THE GREEN CROSS CODE? YOU NEARLY GOT YOURSELF KILLED. CATHY, WHAT'S UP? YOU LOOK TERRIBLE!

OH, TIM!

She told Tim the whole story.

. . . AND I- I TOOK THESE FROM THE DRAWER, TO BUY SOMETHING I SAW IN A SHOP WINDOW. OH, TIM, SHE TRUSTED ME AND I STOLE FROM HER!

NOW, CALM DOWN, CATHY.

8

AND NOW SHE'S DEAD! THAT MEANS I CAN NEVER MAKE THINGS RIGHT WITH HER. I'LL ALWAYS FEEL THAT I'M A THIEF—

NO, LOVE, YOU'RE NOT A THIEF. THOSE TEARS PROVE THAT—

THE IMPORTANT THING IS, YOU STOPPED YOURSELF IN TIME. YOU MEANT TO OWN UP AND GIVE THE MONEY BACK—EVEN THOUGH YOU KNEW THAT IT MIGHT NEVER BE MISSED!

THAT'S TRUE, TIM . . .

ANYONE CAN BE TEMPTED, YOU KNOW. IT'S HAPPENED TO ME—MAYBE EVEN TO MRS STEVENS TOO! I'M SURE SHE WOULD'VE UNDERSTOOD, LOVE. SHE WOULDN'T WANT YOU TO BE UNHAPPY.

MAYBE YOU'RE RIGHT, TIM. THAT'S THE KIND OF PERSON SHE WAS—SWEET AND GENTLE . . .

I'M GLAD I MET YOU, TIM. YOU'VE MADE ME FEEL SO MUCH BETTER.

NO MORE TEARS, THEN! WE'LL SEE SOMEBODY GETS THIS MONEY BACK—THE LAWYERS OR WHOEVER IT BELONGS TO NOW.

OH, AND BY THE WAY, ABOUT SATURDAY—NO FANCY CLOTHES, MIND! THAT'S A STRICT RULE AT ALL MY PARTIES! IT'S YOU I WANT TO SEE, CATHY.

I WON'T FORGET, TIM.

'COS SOMETHING TELLS ME IT'S GOING TO BE THE BEST PARTY I'VE EVER BEEN TO!

IT'S AWFUL, ISN'T IT, WHEN YOU KNOW YOU'VE DONE SOMETHING WRONG THAT YOU CAN NEVER REALLY PUT RIGHT? BUT THEN, WHICH OF US IS PERFECT? AND I THINK CATHY DESERVED HER HAPPY ENDING, DON'T YOU?

THE END

25 WAYS TO CHAT

FED up waiting for the guy you've fancied to chat you up? And no matter how *easy* you make it for him — like always being in the right place at the right time — it never seems to work, does it? All his Royal Highness does is wait till *he's* ready — and by that time you've probably started to fancy someone else! If all this sounds a bit like you're feeling, then don't give up. We've worked out 25 foolproof (well, almost) ways to dazzle him with your line in chat. Interested? Thought you would be . . .

1 You'll need a quick-fire opening line — something witty and totally original. How about, "Where have you been all my life?" Yes, I know it's not terribly original, but what sort of life is it if you can't cheat a little?

Anyway, there are two kinds of answers you'll get to this question.
1. a. "For half of it I wasn't even born."
   b. "Hiding from girls like you."
   c. "In Dartmoor."
   d. Silence — accompanied by a cool, calculating, girl-withering stare.

OR

2. a. "Waiting for a gorgeous girl like you to come along."
   b. "Searching for the girl of my dreams — and now I've found her."

If his answer's in the second category, then success — if it's any of the first lot, oh, well, at least you tried . . .

2 Pretend you're doing market research — all you need for this is a clip board and a few sheets of paper. Oh, and a pen — it's not going to look very impressive if you've got to say, "Ooh, I've lost me Biro. Gimme a shot of yours . . ."

Now all you have to do is market research him. (Don't worry, it's not in the least painful.) All you've got to do is ask his opinion on certain things — like what does he think of girls who're five-foot two, have long blonde hair and blue eyes and've got a 36-22-34 figure.

There's not much point, though, in going through with this idea if you're five-foot eleven in your bare feet, have mousey brown frizzy hair and a figure like the Michelin man in drag!

3 Tell him he's the spitting image of John Travolta (if he's got dark hair) or David Soul (if he's got blond hair). What if he's got red hair? Oh . . . well, tell him he looks just like the man who played Fred Entwistle in "On The Road To The Himalayas."

4 Hypnotise him! Put him into a trance by swinging a watch in front of his eyes and getting him to repeat after you, "You are gorgeous. Will you come out with me tonight?"

5 Be liberated! Phone him up one night and tell him you've got tickets for a disco—would he like to come? (It'd surprise you how often this one works.)

6 Tie him to a lamp-post — and take it from there!

7 Be even more liberated! Next time you're at the disco and a smoochy record comes on, go over, tap him on the shoulder, and say, "May I?" Don't worry, once you've got him on the dance floor, you won't have much chatting up to do — your mind will be on other things.

8 It might take a bit of organising, but try and wangle it so that you speak a really smooth line in patter (there's *bound* to be a book that'll help you in your local library). Just think, you'll dazzle him with your devastating repartee, your witty ripostes, your pungent puns . . .

9 *Don't* mention the weather, whatever you do.

10 Ask him if he's *the* Roger Davenport — the one whose latest film's showing at the Odeon.

11 Offer to share a Polo mint with him.

12 Know absolutely *everything* about motorbikes, football, and the latest hit records. This way you'll never be at a loss for something to talk about.

13 Go for a jog round his block every morning. When he appears at the front door, ready to go to work or whatever, throw yourself on to the ground. Scream and writhe in agony, yelling, "Aoowh, help! I've broken my arm."
(Be careful you don't throw yourself too dramatically on to the ground — you really *could* break your arm.)

HIM UP!

14 Rush up to him in the street and fling yourself in his arms, planting a big smacker of a kiss on his lips. "Ooh, darling, it's been *so* long," you say, hanging on to him for grim death. Then — and only then — do you suddenly look embarrassed, and twitter, "Oh dear, I thought you were someone else."

15 Stage a one-man demonstration outside his house. March up and down with a big placard saying, "I want to speak to you, Reginald Ragsbottom."

16 Pretend you're Superman! Swoop down on him from a great height — the bicycle shed or the roof of your house'll do.

17 Next time you pass him in the street, ever so casually drop your hankie (make sure it's a *clean* one!). OK, it's as old as the hills, but it might just work.

18 Handcuff him to the garden gate and refuse to give him the key till he's asked you out.

19 Next time he's playing football, con all his mates into letting you be referee. This means that you'll be able to show him the yellow card — and take down his name and address.

20 Grab him by the lapels and fling him up against a brick wall. Snarl prettily at him, "Vee haf vays off making you talk."

21 Speak to him only in fluent Portuguese. He'll either find you very, very intriguing — or very, very boring!

22 Slap his face!

23 Offer to come round and listen to him eating his Rice Crispies.

24 Pretend you're a policeman and issue him with a summons. The charge? Refusing to speak to you.

25 Ask him where the nearest glue shop is. When he asks why you want to know, tell him your heart's broken.

And that's the lot! But remember, if at first you don't succeed . . .!

THERE'S nothing old about these fun necklaces! We made them from Das clay, which moulds like Plasticine but dries rock hard. Why don't you have a go, too?

MAKE SOME MOULDY JEWELLERY

If you fancy a crazy bow-tie choker . . .

Mould a piece of clay into the right winged sort of shape, then take a strip of clay and loop it round the narrow centre of the tie. Press it down smoothly at the front but leave a gap at the back to thread a length of ribbon through. (See insert.)

Smooth off any rough edges, mark "folds" horizontally from the centre . . . and leave it to dry.

The next step is to paint it with poster paints. We added little stars and some shading with coloured pencils on top. When the paint's dry cover the bow-tie with a smooth coat of "Varni-Das" varnish, as this gives it a lovely glossy finish.

Lastly, thread a length of ribbon through the clay loop at the back of the tie . . . and wear it!

You'd like to wear your heart on your neck?

Then mould a heart shape from the clay, add a little loop of clay at the back for the ribbon to go through, leave to dry, paint and varnish as before.

He'll remember your name . . .

If it's spelt out in front of his eyes! Roll a slab of clay out flat, about ¼ in. thick. Mark out the letters of your name with a needle — then cut out with a knife. Make a hole in the top of each letter with the needle before drying.

We gave our letters a coat of white poster paint before colouring with several shades of coloured pencil. After being varnished they were threaded on to a length of strong thread along with shop-bought beads. The ends of the thread were knotted together and secured with a blob of glue.

A big bead'll go for a thong.

Beads are easy to make —

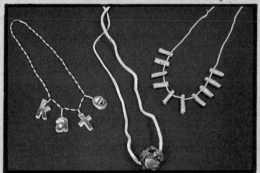

just roll balls of clay in the palm of your hand and stick a thin knitting needle through the centre of each before laying them out to dry. We threaded a big one, decorated with stars 'n' moons, on to a suede thong.

Got your beady eyes on a necklace?

Make one that no-one else'll have by rolling out a long, thin sausage of clay and chopping it into small lengths. Make a hole through one end of each "bead" with a thin knitting needle . . . paint and varnish. Then thread them along with smaller beads, as before . . . and wait for the compliments!

I TOLD HIM

Chris meant the whole world to me. But after the accident that left him crippled everyone told me I should finish with him. They said it was pity I felt now, not love. And, deep down, I reckoned they were right. But as I left him for the last time, I heard him whisper, "I love you," and I had to turn my head away so that he wouldn't see my tears . . .

YOU can't go on like this, Jackie," Mum said in the end. "It's doing you no good at all. You'll just have to finish with him, and forget about him."

It wasn't just Mum, either. Most of my friends were saying the same thing. "It's tough on Chris, but you'd be wasting the rest of your life. He might never walk again."

I suppose, deep down, I knew what they were telling me was true. I'd said it to myself over and over again. The trouble was, I didn't know how I was going to break the news to Chris. I didn't have the nerve to turn my back on him, after all he'd been through.

Losing the use of his legs had been an almost unbearable thing for him to accept. I didn't know whether he'd manage to learn to live with it if I told him I didn't want to see him again, that I didn't want to be tied to an invalid for the rest of my life.

That sounded too cruel, and it wasn't like that really. It was just that Chris had been a special kind of person, alive, active, full of energy, fantastic at sports. That's what brought us together in the first place. I'd been teamed up with him at school to play tennis, mixed doubles.

I'd always looked up to him. He'd got quite a following at our school as captain of the soccer team and champion at the county athletics meetings. He'd been my idol since I was a shy first year and he was already, at fourteen, in the school first team. So I couldn't believe my luck when I found myself as his tennis partner.

And I couldn't believe it when he seemed interested in me, too. It was like a dream come true. He was just so kind and helpful, always ready to laugh, to joke. And sometimes he'd just look at me, and my heart would skip a beat as I thought how lucky I was to have found a love like this.

Later I began to think that it was all too easy, too good to last. Happiness like this had a way of being short-lived.

ACCIDENT!

But I'd never bargained for what happened, that mountaineering accident on a weekend outdoor pursuits course that left his life hanging in the balance for weeks.

They told me that his back was broken. I sat by his bed, night after night, waiting for him to recognise me, hoping that my love and caring could reach him even though he lay still and silent in some strange, unknown world. I prayed that he would live, thinking that all I wanted was to see him open his eyes and smile at me and tell me he still loved me.

Only his smile could dry my tears, only his words of love would give me hope that my life hadn't ended, too. And when he did wake, and stir, and smile, bewildered, at me, I thought that everything would be just as it was before.

I hadn't reckoned for what was to follow. Somehow, all the light went out of Chris when he knew he was crippled, probably for ever. He kept saying that there was no point in living if he couldn't enjoy the things he'd lived for.

He wasn't even angry,

the way he'd been in the past when things went wrong. He was just defeated. It took so long for me to persuade him that he could manage, that there was hope, that I'd stand by him. My love for him would carry him through.

But it wasn't really love, everyone told me. It was pity I felt. How could I love a boy who couldn't walk? Mum said it would be kinder to leave him now, now that he'd got back his will to live. She said I deserved a life, too, and I was too young to waste it on an invalid.

VISITING HIM WAS GETTING ME DOWN

In the end, I came round to their way of thinking. Visiting the hospital every night was really getting me down. I'd lost weight, and most of the time I was too tired to do any of the things I used to enjoy. Perhaps they were right. Perhaps it was pity.

So I told Chris that I'd decided to stop seeing him.

He smiled, just they way I remembered. I'd expected him to be upset, but he just smiled. "That's OK, Jackie," he said. "I understand. I expected it really. Thanks for your help, love . . ." And then he turned away and I got up to leave, hoping that he wouldn't see my tears. After all, it was only pity, wasn't it? Then, just as I moved away, he whispered, "I love you . . ."

That did it. I rushed home to cry, ashamed of myself, ashamed that my love hadn't been strong enough. Mum tried to comfort me, but even her reassurances didn't convince me that I'd done the right thing. I just hoped that Chris would get over me, some day. Then I tried to forget all about him.

I'd forgotten how enjoyable life could be. All my friends rallied round to make sure I had a good time. Before I met Chris I'd gone to discos with the gang, and

Continued on page 16

12

T WAS OVER

"I rushed home to cry, ashamed of myself, ashamed that my love hadn't been strong enough."

ARE YOU AS MAD

Would you be at home in Wonderland, or would you feel topsy-turvy through the looking-glass? Try our special fairytale quiz to see if you'd pass the Alice test!

1. If a white rabbit rushed past you, taking a watch out of its waistcoat pocket and gasping, "Oh dear, oh dear, I shall be too late!" what would you do?
- a. Fall to the ground, shrieking, "I've gone bats! Loony! At last! I've cracked! I knew it would happen one day! It's the strain!"
- b. Take an aspirin and go to bed.
- c. Dash off down the rabbit-hole after it: you *knew* it just had to happen one day!

2. If you shrank to only three inches high after eating a cake labelled "Eat Me," would you . . .
- a. write a very severe letter to the manufacturers, threatening to prosecute them under the Trade Descriptions Act?
- b. borrow some of your little brother's Action Man gear in order to shin up on to the sideboard and ring the doctor?
- c. cry "curiouser and curiouser!" and trot happily about looking for a door three inches high leading off into a magic garden? . . . It must be around somewhere . . .

3. If you were standing in front of your looking-glass one day, and it seemed to go all soft and wibbly and hazy and woozy, and you found you could put your hand right through it, would you . . .
- a. send for the glazier? Rotten-quality glass they make these days.
- b. go and lie down? Really, you must stop reading all these odd books and watching all these weird films . . .
- c. shin through it, quick? You've always wanted to see what there was in that backwards-way room through there!

4. If you were invited to the Mad Hatter's tea party, would you . . .
- a. stay at home?
- b. get into the teapot with the

Dormouse?
- c. make yourself a mad hat to go in? Possibly the coal-scuttle, with a pineapple on top . . .

5. Whilst rushing about looking for the teeny door, you meet a caterpillar sitting on a toadstool and smoking a hookah. Would you . . .
- a. ask it for advice? It's *sure* to know what to do.
- b. squirt it with D.D.T.?
- c. tell it that smoking can damage your health?

6. You play croquet with . . .
- a. mallets, hoops and wooden balls?
- b. flamingoes, soldiers and rolled-up hedgehogs?
- c. who on earth wants to play croquet?

7. Score one point for every one of these you've NEVER met.
- a. The Cheshire Cat.

AS A HATTER ?

b. The Mock Turtle.
c. The Jabberwock.

8. ... you would, this like all was that book a found you if.
a. give up! It's complete gibberish!
b. read it? Books are *all* like that, aren't they?
c. read it — from back to front? You're not stupid, are you? You can do it!

9. Which would you rather have?
a. An unbirthday present.
b. Fish and chips.
c. A treacle well.

10. Arrange the following in the order of least resistance:
a. Humpty Dumpty.
b. Tweedledum.
c. The Queen of Hearts.
d. Tweedledee.
e. The Mad Hatter.
f. The Unicorn.

answers

Well, are you a fit companion for the Mad Hatter? Check out your score and see!

1. (a) 2, (b) 3, (c) 1.
2. (a) 3, (b) 2, (c) 1.
3. (a) 3, (b) 2, (c) 1.
4. (a) 3, (b) 1, (c) 2.
5. (a) 1, (b) 3, (c) 2.
6. (a) 2, (b) 1, (c) 3.
7. *One point each.*
8. (a) 3, (b) 1, (c) 2.
9. (a) 2, (b) 3, (c) 1.

10. No, I don't know, either. Put them all together, and just see what happens!

Ten or under
You'd be at home in Wonderland — you're an inventive nutcase, and a world where things happen backwards

would suit you up to the ground! Trouble is, how on earth do you manage here? — you must find it pretty difficult sometimes!

11-18
I suppose you're quite sane and normal — well, most of the time anyway! But it's great to let yourself go and do silly things every so often, isn't it? For your next escapade, why not try hunting a few jabberwocks?

19 or over
Have you *really* got no imagination at all? Have you *never* seen a Jub-Jub bird, even out of the corner of your eye? If the Frumious Bandersnatch turned up, would you *really* sell it a flag in aid of Concrete Lumps Week and trudge on your way?? Go on, live it up a little!!

15

Continued
from page 12

Chris and I had loved dancing. Now I began to enjoy it again. All the things I'd missed for months were suddenly surrounding me, lights, noise, music, laughter, and more boys than I could cope with.

I hadn't realised what I'd been missing, even though, at odd moments, I'd find myself thinking — Chris will never do this again. Then there'd be a lump in my throat, a memory of tears I'd cried for both of us, and I'd swallow it back and forget, sure that I'd done the right thing.

SOMETHING WAS MISSING

Life really was great for me now. Everyone said how much better I looked, and I felt it. I was back in the school tennis team again, partnering Gary, the new captain. From time to time we'd go out together when I had an evening free from homework, or Pete or Colin, or the gang at the disco. I didn't even have time to catch my breath, let alone think.

Only one little thing kept niggling at me, the fact that nothing I did these days went very deep with me. You know how it is, when you feel happy, but you know something's missing.

That's when I started thinking of Chris again. I'd never felt empty when I'd been with him. And this time I wasn't remembering the liveliness, the wild activity

I'd always associated with Chris.

It was little things that flashed into my mind, the tilt of his head when he was asking me a question, the enthusiasm which lit up his eyes whenever he spoke about anything he enjoyed, the movement of his hands making pictures in the air as he spoke. And there were other things, too, the quiet huskiness of his voice, his gentle smile which made me feel all warm inside, the soft touch of his lips.

It wasn't his boundless energy I missed at all, it was something inside him, a kind of fire, a love of life that I knew would still be there, no matter how broken he was.

No-one else I'd met had that passion for life. No-one else could ever make me feel the way Chris had. And I knew that I needed him, more than ever. I couldn't live without him.

I didn't tell anyone about the way I felt. They'd just have given me advice again, advice that was right for

them, perhaps, but not for me. I didn't care any longer whether Chris was in a wheelchair, I just had to get back to him.

I HOPED IT WASN'T TOO LATE

Somebody had told me, weeks before, that he'd been sent to a special hospital where he'd learn to live with his handicap, and that he'd be there for two or three months. The hospital was right outside the town, in a converted country house on the edge of the moors. But at least it was on the bus route, and I had to see him.

So, that Sunday, telling no-one where I was going, I took the bus out to the hospital. The love we used to have might have gone sour on us. I'd rejected him when he needed me — maybe he wouldn't want me back.

I was ready for the worst, but my fingers were crossed and how I hoped I wasn't too late. Because I was certain of one thing now — my feeling for Chris wasn't pity. I wasn't thinking of my future looking after him, but of being looked after, cared for in a way no-one else could ever care for me. I'd never find a replacement for him.

My heart pounded as I walked up the driveway under the flickering shadows cast by the trees, and suddenly in a patch of sunlight between the trees, on a bench, I saw him sitting alone, staring into the distance. I didn't know what to do, whether to walk on to the reception desk so that I could ask to see him, or just to walk across and surprise him. I stood, undecided, screwing up my eyes against the bright sunshine, trying to focus on him, trying to see whether he'd changed.

"Jackie!" he shouted suddenly. "Jackie!" The happiness and excitement in his voice was all I needed to send me running through the trees towards him, my eyes blurred with tears.

And as I ran, my arms reaching out to him, he stood, straight and tall, and began to run to me, stretching his arms to catch me as I tumbled, breathless and sobbing into the warmth of his touch once more.

"I knew you'd come back," he whispered into my hair. "That's why I had to try . . ." And, gently, he led me to the bench, his arm round my waist, supporting me, as usual, as he always would do.

KID STUFF

Kid Jensen's wife, Gudrun, comes from Iceland, where fish figures largely in the diet, so when Kid comes home, tired and hungry, Gudrun just whips up a tasty fish dish.

13 oz. (368 g) packet puff pastry
7½ oz. (210 g) can mackerel or pilchards
1 oz. (25 g) white bread-crumbs
1 tablespoonful (15 ml) chopped parsley
1 teaspoonful horseradish sauce
Salt and pepper
Egg to glaze

1. Roll out the pastry thinly and cut eight fish shapes (about 5 inches long). Mash the fish and add the bread-crumbs, parsley and horse-radish sauce and season well.

2. Spread portions of the mixture over half the fish shapes, brush the edge of the pastry with egg and press on the second fish shape. Seal the edges firmly and snip over the surface with a pair of scissors to re-semble scales. Brush with egg.

3. Place on a baking sheet and bake at Gas Mark 6, Electricity 400°F, 200°C, for 15-20 minutes. Makes 4 fish. Serve hot or cold.

16

FACE FACTS

BEFORE you can begin to care for your skin, you need to be able to recognise your skin type.

OILY
If your skin looks shiny first thing in the morning, and a tissue pressed against your face shows greasy marks — you've got oily skin. Large, open pores, spots and blackheads are also usually a sign of greasy skin.

DRY
If the skin on your face feels tight and stretched first thing in the morning and after washing, you've got dry skin. You'll also find that extremes of temperature make you go a bit red and may even make your skin a bit flaky.

NORMAL
Not many people are lucky enough to have normal skin — it tends to go a bit dry or greasy, depending on the weather, your diet, and what you've been using on it.

COMBINATION
This is by far the most common skin type. It's both dry and greasy at the same time. The greasiness usually appears on the centre panel, that is, forehead, nose and chin, while the cheeks are dry or normal.

SENSITIVE SKIN
If your skin's sensitive, you'll probably find that you go very red, and using scented skin products may cause your skin to become sore and flaky.

CARING FOR YOUR SKIN TYPE
OILY, SPOTTY SKIN
Scare spots and blackheads to death by keeping your skin oil-free and scrupulously clean.

Use a medicated soap for washing your face, and during the day wipe the greasy areas with a medicated cleansing pad (or a bit of T.C.P. on a piece of cotton wool). This'll prevent a build-up of oil which could block your pores and cause spots and blackheads.

Even though your skin's greasy, you should use a light moisturiser to protect it from the weather, and also to give a better base over which to apply your make-up. Never squeeze spots, instead brighten up dull skin by washing with a grainy facial scrub (damp oatmeal or a teaspoonful of sugar mixed in with a soapy lather are good).

Have a face pack about once a week. Before applying it, cleanse your face then lean your face over a bowl of boiling water so that the rising steam can open your pores. Pat your face dry, then apply your face pack as usual, following the instructions on the pack.

For on-the-spot treatment, use a medicated cream or ointment.

DRY AND NORMAL SKIN
You can treat both these skin types in the same way.

If your skin feels stretched or flaky patches appear after washing, it could be that the soap you're using is too harsh, so try using a gentle soap like baby soap instead.

Some people find that any kind of soap and water leaves their skin feeling tight, though, and if this is the case you'd be best to cleanse your face instead of washing.

Use a fairly creamy cleanser, and make sure you cleanse twice if you're wearing make-up. The first time removes make-up, and the second deep-cleanses your skin. Use a gentle toner to close your pores and remove all traces of cleanser.

It's very important that you use a good, rich moisturiser to protect your skin from the drying effects of the weather. Apply it after washing or cleansing, and whenever your skin feels tight, or flaky patches appear.

Have a face pack once a month, but make sure you choose one specially for your skin type.

COMBINATION SKIN
This is slightly more complicated to look after as you have two different skin types to treat.

First, cleanse all over with a light, milky lotion, then tone the greasy patches (forehead, nose and chin) with a medicated skin freshener.

Finally, moisturise all dry or normal areas on your cheeks with a rich, creamy moisturiser.

Buy tubes of face packs, rather than sachets, as they're more economical when you only use a bit at a time. The oily centre panel will need a face pack treatment more often than the dry area.

SENSITIVE SKIN
Never, NEVER use perfumed soap and water on your face or you'll end up with dry, red patches and your skin will feel sore and itchy.

Choose unperfumed products which're specially formulated for your skin type. These tend to be a little more expensive than other products, but they're essential if you want your skin to look good.

You don't need to have a face pack very often, but if your skin does need to be perked up a bit, choose a product specially for sensitive skin.

WHATEVER your skin type, just remember these three basic rules:

1. Watch your diet — no chips, choccy, etc!
2. Choose products to suit your skin type.
3. NEVER go to bed without removing your make-up.

OK, you ain't got much money, but that doesn't mean you have to walk about with a face like a wet weekend, spreading gloom and despondency! You can still have just as much, if not more, fun, without a penny.

THINGS TO DO WHEN YOU'RE BROKE

★★★★★★★★★★★★★★★

1. Start knitting — scarves, woolly jumpers, gloves. Wool's not all that expensive — and think of the money you'll rake in. Sell your work to your mates — or you could even go round a few of your local shops and see if they're willing to sell your stuff. It's amazing how much people are prepared to pay for hand-knitted clothes.

2. Sell your little brother! It doesn't cost much to put an ad. in your local paper.

3. Find yourself a nice fella who'll offer to pay for absolutely *everything*, all the time (in other words, what you're looking for is a mug!).

4. Check with the children's nurseries and old folk's homes in your area to see if they need any volunteers. You probably won't get paid for it — but helping other people'll take your mind off your own worries!

5. Stand outside a big supermarket, wearing your oldest, tattiest clothes and holding a begging bowl (one of your mum's Tupperwares'll do) in your hand. Hang a poster on a string around your neck saying, *I haven't eaten for three weeks.* All you've got to do now is smile pathetically at all the lovely people coming out of the shop. (Even if you get locked up, at least it'll mean free meals!)

6. Sweet-talk your dad into lending you a hundred quid — well, anything's worth a try!

7. Raid your mum's cupboard and invite a few friends round for a midnight feast. Depending on the state of your mum's cupboards, you could end up with either shrimp paste on Doggy Chew biscuits or pickled caviar on melba toast!

8. Spring-clean the whole house from top to bottom — doesn't matter if your mum thinks you've had a brainstorm! You'll use up a lot

of energy and you'll probably feel a whole lot fitter. And you won't have time to dwell on the fact that you're skint! (And your mum'll be so flabbergasted, she may even lend you a quid!)

9. Do your homework!

10. Instead of moaning about how you've got no money to buy new make-up, make your own! OK, we know you can't go in for mascaras and things, but there *are* lots of things you *can* do. Cleansers, toners and face-y things are quite easy — and you can use your favourite herbs and flowers (try the recipes on pages 86-87).

11. Decide that this week — definitely — you're going to stop eating all the nasty little things that're bad for you and cost lots, too. Baddies include chips, crisps, sweeties, chewing-gum, cakes and biscuits.

Goodies (meaning good for you!) are fresh fruit and vegetables, milk and a reasonable amount of meat, fish and poultry (which you can pinch for free out of the fridge!).

12. If you can swim, now's your chance to try a quick Channel Crossing. It shouldn't take you more than a couple of days — and maybe your Premium Bond'll come up while you're doing it.

13. If you can climb, now's your chance to climb Mount Everest. It shouldn't take you more than a couple of years and maybe your Premium Bond'll come up while you're doing it.

14. Set off on a one-girl hike round the world (the long way, of course). When you get back, you'll be absolutely *inundated* with people wanting to know how you did it — newspaper reporters, TV men, the lot. You'll make a bomb!

15. Get up an hour earlier every day — after a year you'll have been awake for an extra two weeks.

16. Spend two weeks in bed to recuperate from the shock!

17. Choose six objects that you'd like future generations to marvel at. The weird and wonderful things you can get together could include — your little brother, a face pack . . . All you have to do is put them together in a box (tin is best) and bury them in the garden.

18. Write letters — to people you haven't seen for ages, to people you see every day, to the Penpals Patch in Blue Jeans. You can post them when you've saved up for the stamps.

19. Sell some of that junk that's been lying around in your room for ages — those LP's you never play, the books you've read six times, the bed, the curtains, carpet . . .

20. Take up the latest craze that's just swept America, and looks like it'll take off world-wide — rollerdating. Everywhere you go, go on skates. And the best part is when your fella tries to kiss you goodnight — and you zoom off northwards at 60 miles an hour, and he's left standing (if he's lucky) bending limply at the knees!

Feeling Crafty?

TART UP A T-SHIRT

DON'T say you've nothing new or stunning to wear tonight at the disco! If you've got a T-shirt you're halfway to having an exciting new top. We've thought up five different ideas for you to try —

Just For A Scarf!
Cheer up a plain V-necked shirt by giving it a scarf collar.

Simply fold a square silk or cotton scarf in half and, wearing your T-shirt, arrange it over your shoulders so it looks nice and full. Knot the two ends low down on your neckline and pin in place. Take off your T-shirt and very carefully neatly catch the scarf into place at the neck edge. The rest of it should lie neatly in folds.

Put a small row of running stitches along the side of the ribbon, then pull the thread up so that the ruffle is gathered to fit the neck of your T-shirt.

Now, pin the frill to the edge of the neck of your T-shirt, easing out any patches of fullness, then catch in place with tiny, neat hemming stitches at the very edge.

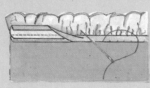

If you like, you can neaten off the edges with bias binding (see sketch).

Fringe Benefits
Either get some ready-made fringing from the haberdashery counter of a large store, or make your own in the following way. Measure the neckline of your T-shirt and cut a length of binding to fit round it. Now sew lengths of wool all along the length of the binding to form a heavy fringe.

Get Ruffled!
Shimmer on the dance floor in a T-shirt trimmed with a satin frill.

Measure right round the neck of your T-shirt. You'll need at least twice this length of 4-inch-deep satin ribbon (depending on how frilling you want to be!).

Sew the fringing on to your T-shirt. A word of warning: T-shirt material is generally very stretchy so it's best to sew things on by hand, gently easing the fabric as you go. You could use a sewing machine on a very loose tension, but only if you're an expert.

Say It With Sequins
Show off your sparkling personality with a sequined message on your T-shirt.

Decide what words you want on your shirt then count up the letters and space them out so they fit across your chest or back. Mark out the letters with tailor's chalk. Mark the place for each sequin with a dot — this'll help to keep your spacing neat and even.

Buy a couple of packets of sequins and also tiny beads with which to hold the sequin in place. Sew on the sequins by bringing your needle up through the T-shirt fabric and placing a sequin on the needle followed by a bead. Slide them down to the fabric and take a stitch back through the centre of the sequin and through to the wrong side of fabric.

Eventually you should have sewn on enough sequins to spell out whatever you want! (No naughty messages, please!)

Zig-Zagged!
This nifty little outfit depends on ric rac braid, again available from a handy haberdashers. Simply sew some braid round the neck and armholes of your shirt using either *very* loose tension on a machine or carefully sewing by hand. Then for a trendy extra, trim some toning ribbon with the same ric rac braid and tie it like a floppy bow tie.

ARIES

LOOKS
Generally a good, strong-looking bloke with a muscular body and lots of thick curly hair. Dresses carefully, but not too vain.

GOOD 'N' BAD POINTS
Highly charged, imaginative and passionate (you've got it made, here!). With all that charm, and his easy-going nature, your family'll find him irresistible, too! Not a sulker, if he's cross about something he'll start shouting — then forget it five minutes later.

Domineering. A real bossy boots which is OK in small doses, but can be a real pain if it's all the time. He's a great one for putting a damper on all your plans and ideas.

GIRLS HE LIKES
The two extremes! Either an independent lady he can admire or a quiet, gentle one he can protect. So if you're in-between these, then you'll have to work hard to catch him!

TAURUS

LOOKS
Taurean guys usually have large frames, yet they hardly ever run to fat. Very tall with fine brown or black hair. Although not conventionally well-dressed, they've got a casual style of their own.

GOOD 'N' BAD POINTS
A very steadfast and faithful guy, you won't find Mr Taurus eyeing up all the talent at a party. A love of the arts makes him a romantic and sensitive partner.

He can be extremely stubborn — trying to make him change his mind is like banging your head against a brick wall, only even more pointless! It's impossible to argue with him.

GIRLS HE LIKES
Taurus isn't a flippant sign and he won't appreciate this in others. You can impress him, though, if you're good with money. And he loves food — so if you can cook, you're a sure-fire winner!

GEMINI

LOOKS
Liable to be slim with twinkly eyes and a friendly expression. Flamboyant in dress, they often stray over the borders of good taste!

GOOD 'N' BAD POINTS
Bustling with energy and ideas, he's very attractive to females and will make a good impression on your friends — maybe too good! It'll either be the romance of the century or a brief encounter — either way it'll be great fun!

An incurable flirt! If you sit and moan he'll drop you like a ton of bricks, and if you try to keep up with him, when are you going to find time to be alone together?

GIRLS HE LIKES
Everyone! And we're not joking! At a party he'll go for the girl who stands out the most. So dazzle him if you can!

CANCER

LOOKS
This guy's appearance may not knock you dead but he's got enough quiet charm to beat the biggest and best competition. He even likes three-piece suits. (Eek!!!)

GOOD 'N' BAD POINTS
A truly good guy, a popular diplomat who'll be impossible to dislike, he'll avoid confrontations like the plague and will refuse to argue — even if you bash him over the head with your bag. Very sentimental — you'll be showered with flowers and boxes of chocs.

Cancer is rather prone to excessive emotionalism and often makes a great romance out of what for you is little more than tender affection. When crossed in love, your mild-mannered Cancerian will turn sour and bitter — and a bit resentful.

GIRLS HE LIKES
Elegant and exotic girls will reduce him to a quivering mass, so play it down. A romantic, shy girl will meet his requirements and so will one who can dominate him, very very slightly. She'll probably have strong maternal instincts.

LEO

LOOKS
Often yer actual tall, dark and handsome — well, dark and handsome anyway! He has a warm expressive aura about him and dresses elegantly and flamboyantly — likes velvet stuff and bright scarves.

GOOD 'N' BAD POINTS
If a Leo likes you — you'll know it. Warm and generous in love, he wears his heart on his sleeve, and can cause a sensitive girl to reel in embarrassment! Lots of presents and treats in store, though, and although it's doubtful whether these are genuine attempts at gratitude or aimed to impress, who cares? Enjoy it while it lasts!

His arrogance! Mr Leo expects his chosen one to love as ardently and passionately as he does, and gets uptight if he thinks he's being short-changed and not getting his fair quota of compliments.

GIRLS HE LIKES
The most beautiful. You don't have to be a natural born one though, and hours in front of the mirror won't be wasted on him. Good taste wins maximum approval.

VIRGO

LOOKS
A slim physique with fine, chiselled features. Good looking but in a slightly cold sort of way.

GOOD 'N' BAD POINTS
Very protective, you'll never feel worried with this bloke. Rather than absolute devotion, his line's more in small thoughtful actions, often overlooked by other boys. He won't sweep you off your feet — but then he won't shatter your heart, either.

A dreadful fusspot. If you're five minutes late he'll want to know all the details, what you were doing, why you couldn't have left earlier, why you didn't wind your watch up, etc., etc. Irritatingly moral — any naughty words (like bother, or fiddlesticks) and you'll be out on your ear!

GIRLS HE LIKES
He's a bit of a perfectionist. Mr Virgo will go for a girl with a sharp and accurate style and a body to match — so no excess weight or sloppy make-up, please.

LIBRA
LOOKS
A well-formed body with broad shoulders and slender hips. Strong sharp features make this the most attractive face in the zodiac. An elegant dresser.

GOOD 'N' BAD POINTS
Great to be seen with, he'll never show you up in public — except to good advantage, that is. A kind character and obliging. At first, anyway, life should be smooth and peaceful — but there's no saying how long this'll last!
Libra often makes vain guys, even more than their female counterparts! You might find yourself waiting outside the gents while he admires his reflection in the mirror! He's very cautious about romance, and sometimes it could be difficult to get the message across to him.

GIRLS HE LIKES
If you look like you've just walked out from a shampoo ad you may be near the mark. Not fond of human flaws or emotionalism — cool, calm and collected is the phrase to remember.

SCORPIO
LOOKS
Mr Scorpio is the dark, intense type smouldering in the corner — he's the one who has the weaker kinds of female fainting at his feet. Very striking — you can't ignore him!

GOOD 'N' BAD POINTS
Whew! There's no playing around with this guy! He won't take no for an answer and will scare off the competition with one threatening glare. Very protective,

once hitched to this one you'll have no worries — except about him, of course!

GIRLS HE LIKES
Shy, pretty girls are favourite, not for him the high-powered career woman — he likes to be the boss.

SAGITTARIUS
LOOKS
Attractive and alert. Usually slim and athletic — and an interest in sport helps to preserve this to a ripe old age! He's a bright, colourful dresser.

GOOD 'N' BAD POINTS
If this bloke takes a shine to you he'll be in love within the hour — don't laugh at him, he thinks he means it! Full of ideas, he'll tire you out, but you'll never be bored. A tolerant guy who won't mind if you do a bit of flirting in between.
He's very fond of fun and games, and likes a run for his money. Once he's got you he's liable to lose interest! Like soul-mate Gemini he's not adverse to a bit of flirting, and any protests will be met with anger — and you won't see him for dust!

GIRLS HE LIKES
Lively and impulsive like himself — he won't stick a stick in the mud! Having career ambitions of your own is fine — especially if it's creative.

CAPRICORN
LOOKS
A dignified, serious and somewhat un-approachable-looking bloke — with a tall skinny body. Don't be put off — that hard shell can be cracked!

GOOD 'N' BAD POINTS
A guy born under this sign will have his eyes on the future, and in relationships he won't be fickle, but generally sticks to one love at a time. Although not overly demonstrative, his heart is in the right place.
Mr Capricorn's got many good points, but generosity isn't one of them. If you

opt for a lengthy relationship you won't go short of anything — but then you won't be breakfasting on champagne and caviare either!

GIRLS HE LIKES
Not for him the dumb blondes of the world. Capricorn lads go for intellect and intelligence in their lady friends — he'll respect any career plans you have of your own.

AQUARIUS
LOOKS
A small frame that can sometimes run to fat. Generous facial features and a friendly manner. Casual, slightly care-less dresser.

GOOD 'N' BAD POINTS
Once captivated, the Aquarian male will abandon everything and focus all his attention on the girl. Trouble is, how to get to him? Sounds cruel, but gaining attention and then playing it cool will have them fascinated.
Aquarians have so many interests that unless they're really in love, they won't pay an awful lot of attention to a casual girlfriend. And some weekends, his favourite sport will definitely take priority. If it looks a bit hopeless, try to turn him into a friend — they're better at that!

GIRLS HE LIKES
He's not bowled over by good looks or even bright intelligence — it's the personality that counts. If you manage to meet his high standards you're home! Best just to play it by ear!

PISCES
LOOKS
A gentle Prince Charming. Very good looking, but in a not-too-obvious sort of way. He'll most likely have fair hair and small, neat features. A romantic, and even slightly effeminate dresser.

GOOD 'N' BAD POINTS
He's possibly the kindest guy in the world. His affection and sensitivity could move you to tears. A great one for cute gestures — opening doors, helping you on with your coat, etc. If you want to finish with him, be very careful about how you break the news.
Pisces is so worried about doing something wrong you'll probably end up making all the decisions, otherwise you'll sit around all evening waiting for him to make up his mind. Most girls *do* like blokes to be a bit masterful — something this one isn't terribly good at.

GIRLS HE LIKES
A passive fella, he'll fall for someone who gets things done — subtly. A great display of brash aggression will send him scurrying.

PUT ON A HAPPY FACE

Just follow our simple step-by-step guide to model girl make-up

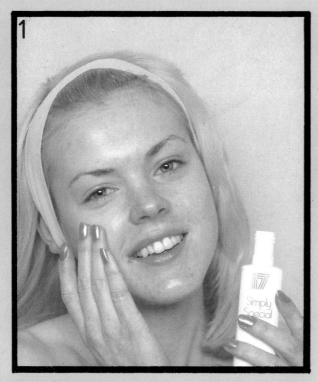

1

After thoroughly cleansing and toning your skin, gently pat some moisturiser on to your face. This'll make a smooth base for your foundation and protect your pores from getting clogged up with make-up.

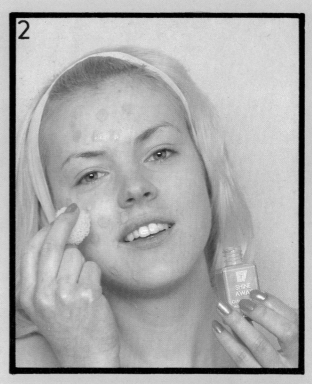

2

Dot foundation all over your face and quickly blend it in with a damp cosmetic sponge, or your fingers. Choose a foundation as close to your own skin tone as possible and make sure it's well blended in round your hairline and under your jaw so that you're not left with a hard obvious line.

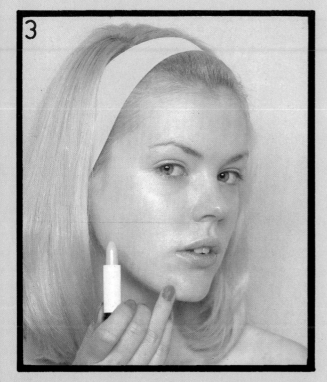

3

Cover up any spots or blemishes on your face with a blemish-covering stick. These are useful for disguising baggy eyes, too. Smooth it into your foundation.

4

Smooth a little cream blusher over your cheekbones and blend well in. Try to position the blusher on the plump part of your cheeks so it looks as natural as possible. (If you're using a powder blusher, apply it later, on top of your face powder.)

5 For a slim-faced model-girl look, suck in your cheeks and lightly brush some shader (a brownish or plum, matt eye-shadow will do) in the hollows. Blend it well in so you don't look like a Red Indian.

6 Pat some translucent powder over your forehead, nose and chin to get rid of any shine. Dust off any surplus powder with a soft powder puff or complexion brush.

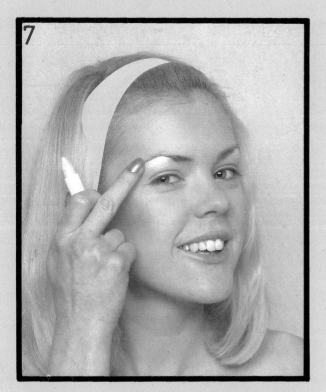

7 Highlight your eyes with a shiny eye shadow in white or cream by gently stroking it along your brow bone. Again this shouldn't be too noticeable so blend it well in.

8 Decide what colour of eye shadow you want to wear and pick a light and dark shade of it. Smooth the light shade over your entire eyelid and fade it up towards your brow bone.

9

Use the darker shade of shadow in the crease of your eye and under the outer edge of your lower lashes. This'll make your eyes look really big.

10

Complete your eye make-up with a couple of thin coats of mascara on your upper and lower eyelashes. Leave the mascara to dry between each coat. Your lashes will look really thick if you put some on to the back of your upper lashes, looking down into a mirror, then put some on to the front of your lashes, looking up.

11

Now for your lips! Choose a shade to match your clothes or to suit your complexion. But remember, if your lips are quite thick use a dark matt shade rather than a light, pearly one. If you like you can outline your lips first with a lip pencil or brush then fill in the centre with your lipstick.

12

Finish off with a smear of lip gloss. Now get into your favourite dress, comb out your hair and smile. You look great!

THEY THOUGHT I WAS NO GOOD!

All my life I'd had to put up with people suspecting me of cheating, accusing me of stealing, always thinking the worst of me – and all because of my sister, Sue.

Then I met Tony, and when my parents began questioning my every move, it was the last straw. I just couldn't take living in Sue's shadow any longer...

THEY'D branded me as no good. I hadn't been given a chance to prove to them that they were wrong. Even my own parents had condemned me because of Sue, and what she had done.

And if that was what they believed, they could live with it for the rest of their lives. I'd show them that I didn't need them, that at sixteen I could fend for myself. After all, being on your own isn't so bad. It means you're free to live life as you want to.

I took a sip of tea and unwrapped the small packet of biscuits I'd bought at the counter. I was glad the motorway café was busy. It meant I didn't stand out as much as I would have done if the place had been empty. Inconspicuously tucked away in a corner, I had time to collect my thoughts.

Getting to London was my intention, and I reckoned it shouldn't be too hard to cadge a lift. After all, once when Tony and I had come here on his motorbike, we'd called the place the crossroads of the world because it was the junction of two motorways.

A lump came to my throat as I thought about Tony. Leaving him behind was my only regret. He meant a lot to me and I could still remember how excited I was the first time he'd so unexpectedly asked me out.

Since then we'd had some good times together and lots of fun. But it had been a light-hearted relationship; he'd never said he loved me, or done anything to suggest he was really serious about me.

Perhaps if he had, it might just have been enough to keep me in the town I'd come to hate. But it was too late to find out now. I'd made my decision and I couldn't turn back.

Even thinking about the place made me feel sick. Over the years so many people there had made my life unbearable. And all because of Sue, my elder sister, whom I could only dimly recall.

Nine years is a long time to remember a sister you haven't seen since you were seven.

But other people couldn't forget, it seemed. The trouble was, they took vindictive pleasure in remembering the bad and completely ignoring all that had been good about Sue. Too many people, without any reason, had seen me as another Sue.

HE WATCHED MY EVERY MOVE

At first, it was little things, like when I bought sweets at our local shop. I'd stand by the counter deciding what to have, only too aware that Mr Green, the owner, was hovering over me, watching my every move. As soon as I touched anything he'd be at my shoulder.

"That'll be ten pence, young lady," he'd say, holding out his hand for the money.

Sue had been caught pilfering and he expected me to do the same. It had become so embarrassing that I'd stopped going to his shop eventually.

When I'd started at the comprehensive, it had become even worse. Sue had been there before me and her shadow had hung over everything I did.

Whenever I got good marks, the teacher would say: "Mandy, are you sure this is all your own work?" It was an accusation of cheating, because Sue had cheated.

If anything went missing at school, and a class search instituted, they always spent twice as much time at my desk as anyone else's. Because, of course, Sue had once been caught with a stolen watch.

None of this had gone unnoticed by my classmates and one in particular, whom I'd named Spiteful Jane, had always made the most of my embarrassment.

"My mum's told me all about your sister,

Mandy. She was a bad lot — never out of trouble. And you're out of the same mould so you're bound to go the same way."

Jane had made me see red so many times. Her snide remarks about me hurt, of course, but it was Sue I'd always ended up defending. I was sure she hadn't been nearly as bad as everyone made out.

One of the few memories I had of Sue was when we'd shared a bedroom and she'd sometimes confided in me, on those nights when we couldn't get to sleep.

She'd admitted stealing from Mr Green, but it had been a dare, and Sue had never been one to back down from a challenge.

She'd been stubborn and strong-willed too, and wouldn't give in to anybody. She'd taken the watch after P.E. one day, to get her own back on the teacher who'd made her run round and round the hockey pitch until she nearly dropped, as a punishment for being cheeky.

Sue hadn't intended stealing it, only hiding it to cause a fuss. But they'd found it on her and no-one had believed the truth.

EVEN MY PARENTS DIDN'T TRUST ME

Young as I'd been, I'd found Sue's ways disturbing, but certainly not wicked or criminal. Now I'm older, I know the word that best described her was tearaway.

She was too full of energy, old for her years, and difficult to handle. But no-one had understood this.

Instead, they simply saw her as a disruptive influence and put her down at every chance. Of course, this made her even more rebellious and things went from bad to worse. Until the day, when she was sixteen, she left home on the back of her boyfriend's motorbike, never to return.

Well, now I, too, had left home at sixteen. And all because I'd been seen as another potential Sue. Originally, much as I'd hated it, I'd been able to face up to the world and the way it treated me. My strength had come from a secure home and parents I thought trusted me.

But even that has gone now, gradually whittled away over the last two or three years. Small things to start with, like discovering they never accepted without question anything I told them. If I said I was going out to tea, or to a disco or the Youth Club with friends, they always checked up behind my back, phoning my friends' parents or the Youth Club leader.

That had been bad enough and had made me shed many tears in private. But when I'd first got to know Tony, and they'd double checked every date I had, it became too much to bear.

On top of that, they always insisted I'd to be home earlier than the other girls of my age. To my surprise, Tony had put up with it for six months, but the crunch had come last week.

Our town held a carnival weekend on the playing field once a year. On the Saturday there was a fancy-dress parade, side-shows and sports, as well as a flower show, organised by the horticultural society, in a specially-erected marquee. In the evening the Youth Club took it over for a dance. This year they'd booked a rock group and a disco. The dance ended at twelve, but it always took at least an hour to clear up afterwards.

"You won't be going to the dance on Saturday, will you?" Tony'd asked early in the week.

"You mean you want to take some other girl?" I'd replied, trying to sound light-hearted, yet dreading deep inside that that was just what he did mean.

"Well, now, that's not a bad idea." He'd

grinned back at me. "But seriously, I was thinking about your parents. You wouldn't be home until after one in the morning. I mean . . ."

I hadn't let him finish.

"You can take it that I'm going, Tony, and what's more, I'll be staying right to the end. They won't say no to such a special occasion."

But I couldn't have been more wrong.

"No daughter of mine is staying out half the night!" Dad had stated firmly.

"But it's a dance for charity, Dad. It's organised by the Youth Club!"

"I'm sure it's all very worthy, Mandy," Mum had interrupted. "But it's not right allowing youngsters like you out that late. It just encourages getting up to all sorts of tricks!"

"Your mother's right," Dad had added. "We don't want you turning out like our Sue did."

"I'm me, not Sue!" I'd shouted back at them.

"Sometimes I wonder," Mum had retorted. "Listen to you now! Talking back to your parents just the way Sue did, showing no respect."

"Next you'll be saying I fancy a boy with a motorbike, just because she did!" I'd flared back, because Tony had a motorbike.

They hadn't disagreed and the argument had raged on and on without me being able to get them to change their decision. Afterwards, when I'd calmed down, I'd made a decision of my own: whatever the outcome, I was going to the dance, and I wasn't leaving before the end.

I FELT JUSTIFIED

It had been a huge success and I'd really enjoyed myself for once. Just as the church tower had struck one, and we'd finished clearing up, our Youth Club leader had come over to me.

"It's nice to see you being able to play a full part in one of our activities for a change, Mandy," he'd said to me.

I'd disobeyed my parents purely for my own pleasure, but his words had made me feel really good. Somehow they justified what I'd done.

Tony had dropped me at the end of my road, so that the noise of his bike wouldn't wake Mum or Dad. Even when I'd crept into the silent house through the back door, the last thing on my mind had been facing my parents in the morning. I felt on top of the world and whatever the trouble, I was sure it had all been worth it.

But the lounge door had been open and they'd been sitting there waiting for me. I'd told them straight out why I was late. The truth — no lies or excuses. They hadn't believed a word. It was really nasty. Mum, in tears, had accused me of all sorts of awful things, and had said despite how hard they'd tried, I was obviously no better than Sue.

"Ask the youth leader," I'd protested, near to tears myself.

But they'd waved that aside, insisting it only proved I'd been there at the end of the evening, but who was to know what Tony and I had been up to before that.

Everything had seemed so utterly unfair. I felt like screaming, it was so frustrating. No way could I get through to them, no matter what I said.

"I wonder why you bother with me at all," I'd finally snapped at them. "You probably can't wait for the day when I leave home like Sue!"

I hadn't waited for their answer. I'd fled to my bedroom and flung myself down on my bed. I just couldn't take any more. All my

Continued overleaf

just like Sue.''

He shook his head.

''Just the opposite. They're really cut up about you leaving — especially your mum. She couldn't stop going on about how it was all her fault.''

''You're trying to tell me I should go back, aren't you?'' I said accusingly. By this time, tears were prickling the back of my eyelids and I had to keep talking to stop them flooding out.

''Sue never went back and she made out all right. I mean, if she hadn't, she'd have come running home again years ago.''

''You mean you've never heard from her since?''

''No, not a word.''

''Then no-one knows where she is or what she's doing; whether she's happy or sad — alive or dead, even!''

That pulled me up sharply. I hadn't thought of it that way before and it was a very sobering thought.

Tony continued: ''I can imagine how your parents must have felt all those years. Having a daughter run away must have been bad enough. But not knowing how she was . . .'' His voice tailed off, leaving me to imagine for myself how they must have felt.

''Ever thought they could be acting, well, over-protective because they're frightened of losing you completely, too?'' he asked suddenly.

Tony looked at me, waiting for my reply.

''Don't you think I haven't tried a million times to prove I'm not Sue?'' I burst out defensively.

''At the moment you're making a good job of proving you are . . .''

Tony didn't finish his sentence. At that moment we both saw the police car pull into the car park. It wasn't a motorway patrol, but a Panda from our town. I knew why they'd come.

I got to my feet.

''I'm not letting them take me back, Tony.''

''Are you sure you know what you're doing?'' Tony looked doubtful.

I nodded vigorously.

''We can go out the back way. They'll never see us if we leave on your bike. Please help me, Tony, I have to do this myself. It's the only way.''

A moment later we were making for the rear exit.

Mum and Dad were both overjoyed to see me.

''I came back,'' I said, when they let me get a word in edgeways.

From the look on their faces, there'd been no doubt they understood just what I meant. Sue hadn't, so I couldn't be like Sue.

''We can all be a little foolish at times,'' Mum said, a smile twinkling through her tears.

It was an admission of the mistake they'd made, and also a mild rebuke. Fighting one foolishness with another wasn't the right way to go about anything.

''You must both be starving,'' Mum said. ''You'll stay for something to eat, of course,'' she added, turning to Tony.

As I looked at Mum, Dad and Tony, I felt happier than I'd been for ages. Now I had three people who I knew loved and trusted me, it gave me new confidence to face the outside world and all the people who would still expect me to be like Sue. With them on my side, it didn't seem to matter so much.

But there's one more thing!

Wherever you are, Sue, are you happy, too? I'd like to know — and so would Mum and Dad.

It only takes five minutes to write a letter. Why not write it today?

Continued from previous page

life, I'd fought so hard to prove to people I was a person in my own right. But now even my parents had joined all the others in believing I was growing up to be another Sue, and the fight had gone out of me.

That was when I'd made up my mind to get away from the town where I'd been born and had grown up, and go somewhere — anywhere — where no-one knew me, where there'd be no-one to point, and say, ''Watch her, she's Sue's younger sister.'' At last I'd be free.

I'd written a note for my parents and sneaked out of the house just after dawn. An early-morning bus had brought me to the motorway café where I sat now, planning the next stage of my journey. My parents might guess I'd make for London, but in a city that size there'd be no way they'd find me.

CONCERNED

''Hello, so you are here!''

The voice broke into my thoughts as I nibbled the last of my biscuits. I looked up to see Tony.

''Your parents phoned mine as soon as

they found your note. They wouldn't believe we hadn't run off together until I went round to see them.''

He pulled up a chair and sat down. His eyes looked straight into mine and I turned my head away, feeling vaguely embarrassed.

''How — how did you find me?'' I stuttered.

''I remembered how we once called this place the crossroads of the world. Where else would you make for?''

The realisation that he was concerned enough to come looking for me made me feel all warm inside. Before I knew it, I was pouring it all out to him, telling him all about the misery I'd been living through, especially at home.

''I'll miss you, Mandy,'' he said when I'd finished. ''Especially now I understand just how hard it was for you.''

That really threw me. He hadn't tried to persuade me to return home. He'd just made me realise how much I meant to him.

''I — I suppose my parents are glad to see the back of me,'' I said, trying to hide my confusion. ''I bet they couldn't wait to tell you how they'd been proved right, that I was

Bags of Florentine work

IF you're able to thread a needle and you'd like to make something a bit different, we'd like to introduce you to Florentine work . . .

Legend has it that when a Hungarian princess married into a noble Italian family she brought with her a beautifully embroidered trousseau. It was so admired that she taught the ladies of the Florentine court how to do it — and so its popularity spread. And now you can follow in their lovely footsteps!

You'll need: single-thread canvas (16 threads to 1-inch size); a blunt-ended tapestry needle, scissors and a selection of wools. (We used Anchor Tapisserie wool mainly, but you could use up odds and ends of fine knitting wool.)

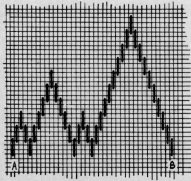

The stitch: each stitch goes over four threads and back one. Following our diagram, stitch out this design from A to B, repeating it until you've filled the width of your bag, or whatever.

Start the second row in another colour just above the first stitch. The threads share the same hole in the canvas so there's no gap. Now, following the first row of stitches, repeat the design as necessary, and continue in this way until you've filled the shape required.

SILVERY CLUTCH BAG

Mark a rectangle on your canvas in ball-point pen. Ours was 25 cm wide by 32 cm deep. Now mark off a triangle at each of the

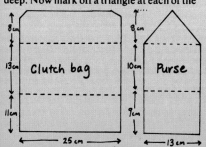

two top corners as this end will form the flap. Don't forget to leave a margin of about 5 cm of canvas round the pattern as the canvas frays a bit. Fill this shape in as explained before, starting and finishing the design at the pen outline.

Cut out the same shape in lining material and sew it to the embroidery with right sides together, leaving a gap. Turn the work right way out, sew up the gap and press.

Fold the bottom end 11 cm up to form the pocket. Oversew the sides. Carefully sew a snap fastener under each corner of the flap (taking care that the stitching doesn't show on the front) and sew the other half to the corresponding places on the front of the bag. And that's it!

PURPLE FLAME PURSE

The purse, or make-up bag, was made in the same way as the clutch bag — only the rectangle was 13 cm wide by 19 cm deep, with a triangle 8 cm deep added to make the flap. It's closed with one snap fastener at the point of the flap.

RAINBOW SPECS CASE

This makes a smashing present (not literally, we hope!) for people like mums 'n' grans.

Simply trace a nice, curved, oblong shape round a pair of specs (or trace an old spec case). Mark the shape on to the canvas, twice, and fill in with the embroidered pattern.

Cut two pieces of lining material to match, as with the bags. Sew them to the embroidered pieces with right sides together, leaving a gap. Pull right sides out, sew up the gaps and press. Lastly, oversew the edges of the pieces together — leaving the top open, of course!

TAPESTRY WAISTCOAT

If you're feeling a bit more adventurous, have a go at making a waistcoat like this. Remember — we made all these things here in the office, and if we can do it, so can you!

First, buy a simple pattern. We used Simplicity pattern No. 8759.

Trace the pattern pieces on to the canvas, being sure to keep the threads of the canvas in line with the "grain of cloth" arrows. Leave a margin of about 5 cm round each piece, and it's also a good idea to cover the edges with sticky tape to stop them from fraying. Trace all the shapings, too — the seam allowance (you'll only embroider up to the stitching line) and any darts (leave the triangle of the dart unembroidered, too).

Use the yarn in lengths of around 40 cm and start sewing up the pattern, following our diagram carefully. Carry the stitching right up to the marked shapings, and when you've finished all the pieces, cut them out on the outside, cutting line. Stitch the darts by hand, pressing them flat — just as you would with normal, thinner material.

Sew up the pieces by hand, following the instructions with the pattern. We'd advise you to make a lining if the pattern has one, as otherwise the inside of your waistcoat will look a bit messy! Now press.

Finally, we added two pieces of silky cord to the front to tie it shut. And there you have it — a very special and unique waistcoat, and it was worth it, wasn't it?

In the mood for a giggle? Well, you've come to the right place 'cos some of our favourite stars have been telling us their favourite jokes . . . and we hope they'll bring a smile to *your* face! Only difference is — we had the type of joke they told analysed to tell us what sort of personality they are. Wonder if they'd find the results so funny . . .

Johnny Fingers of the Boomtown Rats has a stylish joke: "A pretty girl had her hair done in the latest curly style. She thought it looked great, but her fella didn't like it. He said, 'You remind me of a lovely Italian dish'. 'Do you mean an Italian film star?' asked the girl. 'NO . . . I MEAN SPAGHETTI!' said her boyfriend."

On the face of it, he's your typical male chauvinist! And there's a chance that he really *does* think girls are a bit inferior to fellas! He's moody, prone to deep depressions when he becomes convinced the whole world's against him, and in situations like that he will take off by himself to try to think things through. He'll always want to appear unconventional and shock people with the way he looks, because that way he can hide all his own insecurities.

Bob Geldof of The Boomtown Rats asks: "Did you hear about the farmer who took his cow to the vet? The vet asked what was wrong. 'Daisy is very depressed,' said the farmer. 'How d'you know?' asked the vet. 'Well,' the farmer explained. 'I know she's depressed because . . . SHE KEEPS CRYING OVER SPILT MILK!' "

Not so much a joke — more a sort of comment! The way the story's put together indicates this is someone who'll always be good at bluffing his way out of situations and keeping a straight face while doing it!

He'll usually be lucky in whatever he undertakes, but he'll never find it particularly easy to settle down because he feels he should get the most out of life. He's artistic and impulsive, but can give the appearance of being a bit of a loner because he has to get away from it all occasionally.

Debbie Harry of Blondie comes up with: "What do you call a ten-foot-tall budgie? Anything you like . . . AS LONG AS YOU'RE VERY POLITE!"

The joke shows a certain respect for authority, and the person probably has the same attitude. If something's bigger than she is, she'll probably back quietly away from it! She's superstitious and doesn't particularly enjoy being on her own. She's a luxury lover who will always aim for the good things in life, but she cares about her own physical condition, likes sports and could well turn into a keep-fit fanatic!

Kate Bush asks: "What do you get if you cross a sheep with a kangaroo? A WOOLLY JUMPER!"

A-agh! This one's as *old* as "Wuthering Heights"! It's a joke told by somebody who doesn't actually enjoy having to think too much about things she's not interested in. She's far happier keeping herself busy and getting on with her own life.

She'll always enjoy being with close friends, and when she's lonely she'll either pick up the telephone — regardless of the time — and talk to someone, or buzz round to see them. Her own thoughts and dreams are important to her, and whenever she can, she'll put these down on paper — not necessarily in the shape of songs, but just as expressions of the way she's feeling.

Bjorn of Abba has a joke about the weather: "What's worse than when it's raining cats and dogs? WHEN IT'S HAILING TAXIS!"

Thoughtful, romantic and sentimental, the joke shows someone who can also be a bit unconventional, particularly where ideas or theories are concerned. He's ambitious, both for himself and others close to him, but he can frequently be terribly disorganised.

He'll always rely on other people to get him out of the muddle he creates, and he's a very firm believer in fate and luck, but even when things are at their blackest, he'll find some kind of silver lining to cheer himself up with!

MINUTE!

Olivia Newton-John asks: "What do policemen have at teatime? Bread, butter . . . and TRUNCHEON MEAT!"

She still likes simple things, and jokes and games from her childhood will always appeal to her and give her a sense of security. Although she loves her work, perhaps her greatest pleasures come from her home life where she feels she can relax and really be herself.

She's a romantic and a dreamer, but there's a strong streak of self-sufficiency in her which she sometimes uses as a front to hide her natural shyness.

Sweeney star **Dennis Waterman** laughs: "Why do giraffes have such long necks? Because their feet smell terrible . . . and giraffes aren't stupid!"

He really *likes* jokes, and he'll always enjoy a good laugh — though never at the expense of others. He's loyal to old friends, and he'll keep in contact for years. He'll enjoy things like eating out, or propping up the bar in his local where he can just stand and chat to people about the weather, but his private life is important to him, too. He probably likes to *play* jokes on friends, but he's a warm personality who will never knowingly hurt someone, because people are much too important to him.

Liz Mitchell of Boney M says: "Did you hear about the guy who bought a piano? When he got it home it sounded terrible, so he called for an expert. A man came round, looked in the piano and pulled out a fish. 'How did a fish get in there?' asked the owner. 'It's not such a surprise,' said the expert. 'Where else would you expect to find . . . A PIANO TUNA?'"

She's got a bubbly sense of humour and is nearly always enthusiastic about things. She's independent, perfectly capable of looking after herself, and very resourceful, but she also enjoys having people around her. She loves travel and new places, and likes to get out and meet people.

Coincidences will always play a huge part in her general life-style, and no matter how carefully she organises something — other things will always crop up, and she'll have to rethink her plans for no good reason!

Keith Atack of Child says: "Did you know that my brother had to give up tap dancing? Yes, the trouble was . . . HE KEPT FALLING INTO THE SINK!"

Conventional in the extreme, there's probably a strong nostalgic streak in Keith which will mean he'll feel happiest surrounded by bits and pieces that he's collected over the years. His attitude can be brash, uncaring, but underneath all that he's often easily upset by what he *thinks* other people are saying about him. He relies heavily on good friends and will be at his most relaxed in a familiar or family situation.

Lewis Collins of "The Professionals": "Did you hear about the world's worst chef? He made omelettes . . . WITHOUT CRACKING THE EGGS!"

Mmm, well, this *is* a joke — just! And it's told by someone with a really peculiar sense of humour. All sorts of different, zany things make him laugh. He's a very out-going personality who'll always look for the good in any situation — and usually find it. He can laugh at himself, too, and *does* on occasions when he finds himself getting too self-absorbed.

He enjoys company, and can be a bit of a flirt. Although he's ambitious — particularly where his career's concerned — he'll always make time to help a friend in trouble.

Jimmy Pursey of Sham 69 grinned when he told us this one: "Did you hear about the two babies sitting in a pram together? One of them said to the other: 'I know you're a girl and I'm a boy.' The little girl was very impressed.

" 'How can you tell?' she asked. 'Well,' he said, 'it's easy . . . YOU'VE GOT PINK SOCKS ON AND MINE ARE BLUE!' "

He enjoys baffling people by stating the obvious as if it were a brilliant new scientific discovery! Whatever he does, he'll always want to make a big impact on his surroundings, and although he's naturally aggressive and will always fight and argue for what he believes in, there's an uncertain side to him as well.

He hates any kind of insecurity and will be extremely intolerant — to the point of rudeness — if he suspects anyone is simply flattering him.

Finally, **John Travolta** says: "Did you hear about the guy who went to his psychiatrist and yelled, 'You gotta help me, Doc — I keep thinking I'm a giant curtain.' The psychiatrist stayed very cool. He just said, 'OK, Mr Simpson, now the first thing you've got to do is . . . PULL YOURSELF TOGETHER!' "

He's got a really crazy sense of humour but he gets his biggest kick out of traditional things like music-hall jokes. He'll always enjoy variety, particularly in his work, and he's a bit of a perfectionist. Although he likes people a lot, he doesn't feel he needs them around him all the time and he's usually most relaxed when he's on his own. Family ties will remain im-portant to him for the rest of his life, and so will a deep curiosity for finding out about the world and the way it works.

YOU'RE growing out your perm, you've gone off your diet, you haven't been to the disco for weeks, all because you and HE have split up. And suddenly you feel that you're standing still in space and the world is whizzing by without you!

It's lonely out there. But you can join in the fun again if you want to — though it's up to you to make the first few moves yourself.

Action Stations

If you're sad, don't try to pretend you're not! After any kind of loss, you need time to get over it. If you cover up your sorrow with a hearty, aren't-I-having-fun? attitude, the unhappiness doesn't go away, it just goes underground, and can come out months later in all sorts of weird ways.

So lock yourself in your room and bawl your head off. Say his name out loud seven hundred and thirty times. Punch your pillow to bits — and generally admit to yourself that you're not too happy with the situation!

Sounds a silly suggestion? Give it a try. By the third night, you'll find it hard to squeeze any tears out, the sound of his name is no longer music to your ears, and you're even beginning to feel sorry for your pillow!

Once you've shouted him out of your system, you're ready to talk him out. Invite a friend round (friend — you know, one of those people you used to stand up if he asked you out the same night). Have a coffee, and tell her every detail of the break-up.

The great thing about friends is that they love listening to this sort of stuff — first time round, anyway! Tell her what he did, what you said, what he said next, and ask her where she thinks you went wrong. (Don't contradict her advice — it's too late to take it, and she may make a point that you missed!)

Face Up To It

One thing you have to realise, of course, is that now Lover Boy has left, distance suddenly makes him seem even more attractive in your eyes. You forget his dirty ears, his gum-chewing, his habit of borrowing *your* money to take you out. And you remember only his warm hand holding yours on a cold night, his silky eyelashes, and the time he said he'd rather be with you than watch Liverpool play at home.

This is a natural reaction, but it isn't a realistic one! True, he had good points — that's why you fancied him! But it was the bad points you broke up over! So be ruthless. Concentrate on his borrowing,

ONE IS A LONELY NUMBER

You've split up with your guy and you feel as though you're standing still in space with the world whizzing by. If you want to join in the fun again – here're a few hints on how to do it!

his lateness, his awful friends — and work yourself up from sad to MAD!

A creep like that has the good luck to go out with you and then HE CHUCKS YOU??!!! What a moron! What a cheek! Who does he think he is? He's lucky you even stayed in the same room with him, let alone went out with him! He must be crazy! Want him back? No thank you! He's gone and you're GLAD! (Shouldn't think there'll be much of your pillow left by now.)

Glad All Over

Some break-ups do bring you a real sense of relief. No more sitting about feeling like the Invisible Woman in smoky pubs or cafés while he concentrates on his friends, or hanging around the side-lines, freezing, watching him play football, or rugby, or whatever; no more wet, off-centre kisses, no more of his stupid jealousy to cope with. Sometimes the sense of freedom can make you feel quite high!

Back In The Swim

No matter how you feel to begin with, though, sooner or later you'll want to get back into circulation — but watch out for the pitfalls!

Don't try to get him back. Few breaks come suddenly, and you must have felt this one coming. That doesn't mean you'll never be friends again — just that you need a rest from each other *now*.

Some girls are so affronted at being dropped that they wheedle and plead with the boy to go out with them again — and then they chuck *him*! But it's a silly sort of revenge, and it can backfire — he may figure out your motives and get in first *again*. Result as above: two break-ups and twice the pain!

Don't try to find an instant replacement. There will be a

hole in your life, but a different boy can't be expected to fill it in exactly the same way as the first. So don't pester a new date to go steady right away.

Going out with sixteen different boys in a fortnight isn't a good idea either (always supposing you could find the sixteen boys!). You'll just get confused by all that variety. And you'll probably end up with a reputation as a girl who can't say no!

Ideally, you'll go around with your girlfriends more, and have dates with three or four boys on a strictly non-serious level. Since you're not looking for Mr Right, you won't insist on perfection in any one fella — and you'll be more of a friend than a girlfriend.

All Systems Go!

If your heart has been badly battered, you may find it hard to feel *anything* for a while. But this numbness can have advantages — it can help you speak to people you've been shy of, because now you won't care if they respond or not! Or it could let you volunteer for a sponsored walk without worrying what people think.

Walking's very good at a time like this: there's something about a steady plod-plod-plod that soothes the mind, calms the heart — and gets your legs into shape too!

This is what Jean did. "Two months after splitting with Alan, I still felt dead inside. Then I passed a stall in town where people from the local mental hospital were asking for volunteers.

"At first I thought the kids looked a bit odd, but now I honestly don't notice. I've had a couple of nice boyfriends since then, but I wouldn't give up my two hours a week with the kids."

Andrea found a solution closer to home.

"I was sunk in gloom and pretty rotten to live with. I was going to moan to my mum that the bathroom was dirty. But instead I decided to clean it myself. It looked tremendous when I'd finished, and I was so hot and sticky I had to have a bath!

"But for some reason, I felt cheerful for the first time in weeks. I suppose the physical work cancelled out all that mental brooding. Anyway, I do it every week now. I sing at the top of my voice and I've almost forgotten who I'm trying to forget!"

Andrea's touched on the truth there. After a period of mental brooding, physical action — especially if it's of a kind you've not tried before — is just the thing for getting you on an even keel again. And then you're all ready to set sail in search of new adventures — with a little more experience of how to handle them●

Trapped in the Dark

HI, TESS! GREAT TO SEE YOU! WELL, THIS IS THE FLAT— WHAT D'YOU THINK OF IT SO FAR?

OH, IT'S TERRIFIC, SUE. JUST HOW I IMAGINED A SMART CITY FLAT WOULD LOOK. I REALLY APPRECIATE YOU 'N' EMMA LETTING ME SHARE WITH YOU.

OUR PLEASURE! WE BOTH PREFERRED THE IDEA OF SOMEONE I KNEW FROM MY OLD HOME TOWN INSTEAD OF ADVERTISING FOR A TOTAL STRANGER TO LIVE WITH US.

DID I TELL YOU EMMA'S AN AIR HOSTESS? SHE'S OFTEN AWAY FOR DAYS AND WEEKS AT A TIME SO WE'LL HAVE PLENTY OF ROOM. AND ANY NIGHT YOU WANT TO BRING A BOYFRIEND HOME I'LL ARRANGE TO BE OUT WITH MY BLOKE.

It was Tess's first time in the city, and she felt a bit apprehensive as she listened to her cousin chatter on about her steady . . .

. . . AND HIS DESIGNS FOR THE BOOK JACKETS WERE SO GOOD THAT HE'S BEEN PROMOTED. HE'S GOING AWAY ON AN AMERICAN TRIP NEXT MONTH.

THANKS, BUT I'M SURE I'LL BE TOO BUSY WITH MY NEW JOB TO BOTHER WITH BOYS FOR A WHILE.

HECK! SUE AND HER CROWD LEAD SUCH A GLAMOROUS LIFE I HOPE THEY WON'T THINK I'M A HOPELESS COUNTRY BUMPKIN. I'D GIVE ANYTHING TO GET OVER MY SHYNESS AND BE LIKE THEM!

At first she felt really lost in her new job . . .

I FEEL SUCH AN OUTSIDER! EVERYONE ELSE SEEMS SO COOL 'N' CONFIDENT . . . AND THEY ALL KNOW EACH OTHER, TOO. I WONDER IF I'LL EVER GET USED TO IT?

But as the day wore on she began to relax . . .

THAT LAST LOT OF INVOICES WAS FINE, TESS, AND HERE'S THE NEXT BATCH. I CAN SEE WE'LL GET ALONG WELL TOGETHER. YOU'RE A GOOD WORKER AND PRETTY WITH IT, AND THAT'S EXACTLY WHAT WE NEED AROUND HERE!

TH—THANK YOU, STEVE.

MMM . . . BEAUTIFUL, IN FACT. YOU'VE GOT LOVELY SKIN, TESS . . . LIKE A PEACH.

I . . . I DUNNO ABOUT THAT . . .

OH, I WISH HE WOULDN'T DO THAT! I EXPECT IT'S THE WAY THEY ALL TALK WITH EACH OTHER AND THEY PROBABLY THINK NOTHING OF IT, BUT I'M NOT USED TO IT!

As he left one of the older girls came over . . .

DON'T TAKE ANY NOTICE OF STEVE. LOVE. HE THINKS HE'S THE OFFICE ROMEO BUT HE'S HARMLESS REALLY. IF YOU JUST LAUGH AT HIS SLUSHY REMARKS HE'LL COOL OFF OK.

THANKS, I'LL REMEMBER THAT THEN.

But Steve hung around her for the rest of the day and was waiting outside at five . . .

A LITTLE BIRDIE'S TOLD ME YOU'RE LIVING JUST ROUND THE CORNER FROM ME. SO YOU MUST LET ME GIVE YOU A LIFT HOME AND SAVE YOURSELF A BUS FARE!

UM . . . WELL, THAT'S VERY KIND OF YOU . . .

HOW CAN I REFUSE WITHOUT SOUNDING RUDE? I SUPPOSE I SHOULD STEER CLEAR OF HIM IF HE'S SUCH A WOLF, BUT HE IS KIND OF GORGEOUS . . .

And when she got home . . .

NOW YOU KNOW MY ADDRESS SO IF YOU WANT ME FOR ANYTHING AT ALL JUST SHOUT. IN FACT, I MIGHT LOOK IN FROM TIME TO TIME TO SEE IF YOU'VE ANY LEAKY TAPS, JAMMED WINDOWS . . .

THANKS AGAIN, AND GOODNIGHT, STEVE.

NO! I WON'T LET MYSELF FALL FOR THIS GUY. HE'S TOO MUCH OF A FAST WORKER, A SMOOTHIE WHO'D LOSE INTEREST AS SOON AS I DID.

She got in to find Sue whirling round the flat, packing a case. Her boyfriend had invited her up to London for his firm's dinner-dance . . .

SO I'VE TAKEN A COUPLE OF DAYS OWING TO ME AND I'M STAYING OVERNIGHT. I'M REALLY SORRY TO DASH OFF AND LEAVE YOU ALONE ON YOUR FIRST WEEK HERE, TESS, BUT YOU DO UNDERSTAND?

YEAH, IT'S OK. I WOULDN'T WANT TO MISS A SPECIAL DO LIKE THAT, EITHER. I KNOW WHERE EVERYTHING'S KEPT SO THERE SHOULDN'T BE ANY PROBLEMS.

But later, when Sue had gone, a little worry crept in . . .

POLICE ARE SEEKING A MAN IN CONNECTION WITH AN ATTACK ON A TEENAGE GIRL LAST NIGHT. THIS IS THE LATEST OF A SERIES OF ASSAULTS ON GIRLS IN THE MORLEY DISTRICT WHERE THE ATTACKER HAS BEEN BREAKING AND ENTERING BEDSITTER FLATS . . .

THE MORLEY DISTRICT? BUT THAT'S HERE! I MUST BE CAREFUL TO LOCK UP TONIGHT.

DRAT! THERE'S NO TEA AND SUE'S OUT OF COFFEE, TOO. THAT MEANS I WON'T HAVE A HOT DRINK TONIGHT OR FOR BREAKFAST UNLESS I POP OUT TO THE CORNER SHOP. IT SHOULD BE SAFE ENOUGH, THOUGH—IT'S ONLY SIX-THIRTY AND THERE'RE STILL LOTS OF PEOPLE AROUND.

All the same, she hurried back fast . . .

HE . . . HE COULD BE ONE OF THOSE BLOKES! BUT WHOEVER HE IS HE WOULDN'T DARE . . . NOT IN A BRIGHTLY-LIT STREET LIKE THIS . . .

He chatted on as if they were old friends, but she lost her nerve . . .

I CAN'T STAND IT . . . G—GOTTA GET OUT OF HERE!

HEY, COME BACK!

NO WAY!

HELP! HE'S CRAZY! PLEASE HELP ME . . .

WAIT A MINUTE, I ONLY WANT TO . . .

TESS! WHAT'S WRONG?

STEVE! OH, THANK GOODNESS IT'S YOU! THAT BLOKE WHO'S BEEN ATTACKING GIRLS— HE'S AFTER ME!

QUICK, HIDE HERE IN THE SHADOWS!

THERE, HE'S LOST US.

BUT, STEVE, SHOULDN'T YOU GET AFTER HIM IN CASE HE ATTACKS SOME OTHER GIRL?

NO, I'M GOING TO BE FAR TOO BUSY WITH YOU, MY DARLING.

I CAME HERE SPECIALLY IN THE HOPE OF SEEING YOU THIS EVENING. YOU JUST DON'T KNOW THE EFFECT YOU HAD ON ME WHEN YOU WALKED IN THE OFFICE.

STEVE, LET GO— YOU'RE HURTING MY ARM! PLEASE . . . STEVE!

As she screamed a figure lunged out of the darkness and knocked Steve flying . . .

HANDS OFF, YOU SCUM!

AARGH!

Then everything was happening at once. The lights came on, there were policemen rushing up from all directions and Steve was in handcuffs.

YES, WE'VE SUSPECTED HIM FOR SOME TIME, MISS. TONIGHT WE WATCHED HIM FOLLOW YOU FROM THE SHOPS AND HANG ABOUT AT THE ENTRANCE TO THE BLOCK OF FLATS. WE WERE ABOUT TO NAB HIM WHEN THE POWER FAILED AND HE GAVE US THE SLIP. IT'S LUCKY YOU HAD YOUR BOYFRIEND TO PROTECT YOU.

She had to go along to the police station to make a statement with her rescuer. And afterwards . . .

HOW ABOUT COMING FOR A COFFEE IN MY FLAT—AS AN INVITED GUEST THIS TIME, INSTEAD OF AN INTRUDER WHO PINCHES MY BAKED BEANS!

NO, I LIVE NEXT DOOR TO SUE 'N' EMMA AND YOU WENT IN THE WRONG DOOR. WE KNEW THE KEYS WERE THE SAME BUT IT DIDN'T SEEM TO MATTER TILL NOW!

FIRST OF ALL I THOUGHT YOU WERE A BURGLAR, THEN WHEN I SAW THE BEANS TIN I TOOK YOU FOR SOME HOMELESS AND STARVING WAIF SHELTERING FROM THE COLD.

YOUR FLAT, KEITH? BUT YOU WERE IN OUR FLAT!

CHEEK! DO I LOOK LIKE A WAIF?

ANYTHING BUT! NOW I SEE YOU PROPERLY YOU'RE KIND OF GORGEOUS, IN FACT!

WHAT THAT COPPER WAS SAYING ABOUT ME BEING YOUR BOYFRIEND—I THINK WE SHOULD DISCUSS IT FURTHER, DON'T YOU?

MMM . . . MAYBE WE SHOULD, KEITH.

THERE'S NO-ONE AROUND IN CASE I NEED RESCUING FROM MY RESCUER. BUT SOMEHOW, I DON'T THINK THAT'S GOING TO MATTER . . .

The End

36

HOW TO FLIRT

IT'S a great art, is flirting, and if you can master it, you can be sure of plenty fun.

Let's begin with the basic flirt. Here you have your flirter — the person doing the actual flirting, and the flirtee — the person who is being flirted with.

It all starts with what is known as eye contact. Y'know the sorta thing — you look at him, he looks at you and kapowee zing zap. Something goes tingle in your tummy. Could this be love? Well, perhaps not, but who cares, whatever it is, it's nice!

Some flirtings never get past the eye contact. Maybe you're upstairs on the bus and he's out there in the queue waiting for the number 37 and all you do is look and sorta smile before you're whisked off up the High Street, leaving him still standing gazing after you wistfully.

The great thing about flirting is you can do it anywhere, any time and with anybody — providing, of course, that he's male!

You can flirt with the old man who runs the sweet shop down the road, the little boy next door, your dad, with old flames, new flames, current flames — even with your best mate's best flame! (Please note, here sometimes you have to flirt and run!)

After your eye contact you move on to actual speaking. Of course, your eye contact can say a lot, but this is usually the sorta naughty thing that's best left unsaid!

The thing about flirting conversations is that it's not what you say — it's all the cheeky things you don't say. It's what you're secretly thinking that's interesting, and even more interesting what you're imagining he might be secretly thinking!

He says, "Hi." Thinks: wouldn't mind gettin' her all alone in the back of my ol' man's Cortina.

You say, "Well, hi." Thinks: you've got a smashing smile, wouldn't mind gettin' stuck in the lift with you!

He says, "We-ell, hi."

Thinks: wow! she's a lovely mover.

You say, "Ha, ha (slight wiggle) hi." Thinks: oooh, he's got a nice bum, I like a guy with a nice bum!

It's easy to see how any eavesdropper might find this boring, but to the two flirting parties it's great fun and all because of the naughty things they're not saying to each other!

There is another type of flirting chat, and that is when you both banter wittily about one thing and mean something totally different.

For example, he could say, "Do you like saxophones?" Or it might be do you like Bognor Regis, chip butties, Cocker spaniels, lupins or whatever.

Then you reply, "No, as a mattera fact I'm more into tubas, Southport, soggy tomato sarnies, Great Danes or marigolds." It's the naughty secret meanings that you're both reading into this conversation that's giving you both a buzz, and why not? It's buzzes like this that make the world go round.

Now, having become an accomplished ordinary flirter, it's time to move on to the multi-flirt. This operates on the same principles as before, only now you have more of it! There being more chaps to flirt with, there'll naturally be more eyes to make contact with, and more cheeky, silly banter going round.

Here, you might think you have to be wittier and wigglier than ever, but remember you're the only girl with all these guys so the ball's in your court. It doesn't matter how witty you are really 'cos you've got all of them fighting for your attentions. Great! There's nothing quite so nice as being the only girl in a crowd of flirtatious fellas and being lavished with their attentions and flattery.

Someone says, "Wot ya doin' tonight, Mavis?" Someone else says, "She's comin' out wiv me, in't she?" Someone else chips in, "No, she isn't, she's comin' out with me, arn't ya?"

And so on, while you just wiggle and coo and act hard to get. And hoping to get the Flirt of the Year award, 'cos flirting's fun and it's friendly and it's non-fattening and it's quite the best way to get through a dreary, grey, penniless day!

The Look

TRAVIS FOOL

Dave Lee Travis's wife, Marianne, is Swedish, so this Swedish Fruit Fool gives her a taste of home.

1 lb. (400 g) redcurrants or blackcurrants or 8 oz. (200 g) of each
1 lb. (400 g) raspberries
6 oz. (150 g) sugar
1 oz. (25 g) cornflour
½ pint (250 ml) double cream

1. Cook all the fruit with one cup of water and the sugar until it's soft. (If you use tinned fruit, you won't need the sugar.) Using a wooden spoon, press the cooked fruit through a sieve into a saucepan.

2. Put 3 tablespoonfuls of the fruit in a cup with the cornflour and mix thoroughly. Add this to the rest of the fruit and stir in well, over a gentle heat, and cook for three minutes until the cornflour thickens the fruit.

3. Leave to cool with sugar sprinkled on top, to prevent a skin forming, then pour into a glass dish. Decorate with whipped cream just before serving.

Serves six

BLUE JEANS' BIG BOX

DASH IT!

Here're the names of some top TV programmes — the reason they look so funny is 'cos half the letters are missing! See if you can fill in the spaces.

1. T–– B–ON–– W––A–.
2. C–A–L––– –N––LS.
3. –A–P– –A–S.
4. G––ZZ–– A–A–S.
5. –O– O– –H– P–P–.
6. ––I––. (Clue: They're great with salt and vinegar!)

WHAT'S THE CONNECTION?

What links the following?
1. Noel Edmonds and Lene Lovich.
2. Kate Bush and Emily Brontë.
3. Joe and Frank.
4. Jock Anderson and Snowey White.
5. Noah and Nellie.

YOU'RE BOOKED!

OK, now we're going to see how much you really *do* know. Who wrote the originals of these?
1. Worzel Gummidge.
2. Watership Down.
3. Kidnapped.
4. Tarzan.
5. The Famous Five.
6. Rebecca Of Sunnybrook Farm.

WHICH . . .

1. DJ had a hit with his own version of The Floral Dance?
2. DJ has a wife called Gudrun?
3. DJ was married to one of the stars of Robin's Nest?
4. DJ once had a sidekick called Flynn?
5. DJ liked to be called The Hairy Monster?

QUICK, QUICK!
2. Who, or what, is Fiver?

A BUNCH OF COMMONERS

What do the following groups of people have in common?
1. Reginald Bosanquet, Anna Ford, Ivor Mills.
2. Kenny Dalglish, Archie Gemmill, Lou Macari.
3. Bruce Forsyth, Morecambe and Wise, Michael Crawford.
4. John, Ben, Jim.
5. Jimmy Tarbuck, Nicholas Parsons, Ted Rodgers.

QUICK, QUICK!
3. Name the two resident captains on Michael Aspel's quiz show, Give Us A Clue.

QUICK FLASH!!

1. Who's this happy little fellow?
2. Name the zany programme he hosted.
3. What's the name of his galactic explorer?

QUICK, QUICK!
1. What's the name of Captain Kirk's spaceship in Star Trek?

QUICK FLASH!!

1. You could say this guy's nuts! Why?
2. What's his name in real life?
3. What's the name of the detective who keeps hounding him?

SALE OF THE CENTURY!

Everyone loves quiz programmes — they give you the chance to see how much you know. So, as a special treat, we've brought you our own mini-version of Sale Of The Century. Have a go and see how well you'd do. On your buzzers, get set — go!
1. What do you call someone who has a compulsion to steal?
2. If you're suffering from insomnia, what's wrong with you?
3. Is organdie (a) a musical instrument, (b) a flower, (c) a fine muslin?
4. "Doctor –––, I presume?" What's the missing name?
5. What do the symbols H_2O represent?
6. What would you do if you were given some castanets — eat them, wear them, play them or drink them?
7. What is measured in hands?
8. Who painted the Mona Lisa?

to the goggle box.

GAME!

QUICK FLASH!!

1. Before he got hairy, which character did this actor play?
2. What was the name of his daughter in that series?
3. In the series, Chalk And Cheese, what was the surname of his next-door neighbours?

CELEBRITY SQUARES!

Name the stars in this big-box game!

1 2 3
4 5 6
7 8 9

ANSWERS

YOU'RE BOOKED!

1. Barbara Euphan Todd. 2. Richard Adams. 3. Robert Louis Stevenson.

WHAT'S THE CONNECTION?

1. Lucky Numbers! 2. Wuthering Heights. 3. They're the Hardy Brothers. 4. Dick Barton – both of them are his assistants. 5. The Skylark!

QUICK, QUICK!

1. Starship Enterprise.

QUICK FLASH

1. Kenny Everett. 2. The Kenny Everett Video Show. 3. Captain Kremmen.

DASH IT!

1. The Bionic Woman. 2. Charlie's Angels. 3. Happy Days. 4. Grizzly Adams. 5. Top Of The Pops. 6. Chips.

A BUNCH OF COMMONERS

1. They're all newsreaders with ITV. 2. Footballers in the English First Division. 3. They all "defected" from the BBC and now star in programmes on ITV. 4. They're all Waltons! 5. Hosts of TV quiz shows.

QUICK, QUICK!

2. One of the rabbits in Watership Down.

QUICK FLASH!!

1. He plays a character called Hazell! 2. Nicholas Ball. 3. Choc Minty.

WHICH . . .

1. Terry Wogan. 2. Kid Jensen. 3. Tony Blackburn. 4. Noel Edmonds. 5. Dave Lee Travis.

CELEBRITY SQUARES

1. Cheryl Ladd. 2. Elvis Costello. 3. Leif Garrett. 4. Bob Monkhouse. 5. Willie Rushton. 6. Miss Piggy. 7. Spike Milligan. 8. Lulu. 9. Bryan Ferry.

QUICK FLASH!!

1. Frank Spencer. 2. Jessica. 3. Scott.

SALE OF THE CENTURY!

1. A kleptomaniac. 2. You can't sleep. 3. (c) a fine muslin. 4. Livingstone. 5. Water. 6. Play them. 7. The height of horses. 8. Leonardo da Vinci.

(If you scored between 6 and 8 you've won a night out with Nicholas Parsons, between 3 and 5 a weekend with Nicholas Parsons, and if you scored 0, 1 or 2 – a lifetime with Nicholas Parsons!!)

QUICK, QUICK!

3. Una Stubbs and Lionel Blair.

4. Edgar Rice-Burroughs. 5. Enid Blyton. 6. Kate D. Wiggin.

39

SHE THOUGHT SHE WAS LOSING HIM

MIKE AND ANNE HAD BOTH DONE WELL AT SCHOOL AND NOW THEY WERE GOING AWAY TO COLLEGES IN DIFFERENT TOWNS . . .

THIS IS OUR LAST EVENING TOGETHER. IT MAKES ME FEEL SO SAD . . .

YOU'RE MAKING IT SOUND LIKE THE END OF THE WORLD, BUT IT ISN'T REALLY, YOU KNOW.

IT'S QUITE EXCITING TO BE MAKING A FRESH START IN A COMPLETELY NEW PLACE.

OH, MIKE, HOW CAN YOU SAY THAT WHEN I'LL BE IN LEEDS AND YOU'LL BE MILES AWAY IN MANCHESTER? YOU SAID YOU'D MISS ME, BUT I DON'T THINK YOU WILL.

DON'T BE DAFT, LOVE—OF COURSE I'LL MISS YOU! I RECKON YOU'VE GOT A DOSE OF THE GOODBYE BLUES. WELL, I HAVE, TOO, BUT IT JUST MAKES YOU FEEL WORSE IF YOU GIVE IN TO THEM. C'MON, LET'S GO FOR A WALK—IT'LL MAYBE MAKE YOU FEEL BETTER.

D'YOU HONESTLY THINK I'D FORGET MY BEST GIRL THAT EASILY? I'LL BE THINKING OF YOU ALL THE TIME.

IF ONLY WE WERE GOING TO THE SAME PLACE . . .

YOU KNOW WE TALKED THAT OVER AND IT'S JUST NOT PRACTICAL.

I FEEL KINDA SAD ABOUT LEAVING HERE. I CAN'T HELP REMEMBERING ALL THE GOOD TIMES WE'VE HAD. BUT WE'LL BE ON HOLIDAY BEFORE YOU KNOW IT. AND, AFTER ALL, OUR COLLEGES AREN'T THAT FAR APART, I'LL BE ABLE TO SEE YOU SOME WEEKENDS.

YOU WILL?

MANCHESTER'S THE BEST PLACE FOR MY SCIENCE DEGREE, BUT YOUR FASHION DESIGN COURSE IS BETTER AT LEEDS.

YES, YOU'RE RIGHT.

I JUST WISH YOU WEREN'T SO CHEERFUL ABOUT IT, THEN I'D BE MORE CONVINCED.

WE LOVE EACH OTHER, ANNE. BEING APART WILL ONLY MAKE OUR FEELINGS STRONGER.

I LOVE YOU SO MUCH, MIKE, I WISH I COULD STAY IN YOUR ARMS FOR EVER.

Next day she arrived at the college.

IT'S ALL SO BIG AND I FEEL VERY ALONE. I'D BETTER FIND MY WAY TO THE MAIN HALL. THEY SAID THERE'D BE SOMEONE THERE TO MEET THE NEW STUDENTS.

Anne became even more depressed as she finished off her packing.

IT'S A PRESENT FROM CHRIS. SHE SAYS IT'S FOR PLAYING HOSTESS TO ALL MY NEW FRIENDS. MOST OF MY MATES ARE GOING AWAY, BUT THEY'RE ALL LOOKING FORWARD TO IT. THERE MUST BE SOMETHING WRONG WITH ME.

I'M JUST SO SCARED ABOUT THE WHOLE THING! I WANT TO STAY HERE, BUT I DAREN'T. MUM AND DAD HAVE SUCH HIGH HOPES FOR ME. I HAVE TO GO THROUGH WITH IT.

THE NEXT FEW HOURS WERE A WHIRL OF DIRECTIONS, INSTRUCTIONS AND INFORMATION SHEETS. THE FIRST YEAR STUDENTS ALL LIVED IN THE SAME BUILDING. SIX STUDENTS SHARED A KITCHEN, BUT EVERYONE HAD THEIR OWN BEDROOM.

ALONE AT LAST, THANK GOODNESS! IT'S SUCH A STRAIN BEING WITH ALL THOSE STRANGERS. AND I'LL BE HERE FOR THE NEXT TWO YEARS. I DON'T THINK I'LL EVER GET USED TO IT.

I'M MISSING MIKE ALREADY. I WONDER HOW HE'S FEELING. NEITHER OF US HAS EVER BEEN AWAY FROM HOME BEFORE— EXCEPT ON SCHOOL TRIPS OR HOLIDAYS. AND THEN WE WERE WITH EACH OTHER, OR PEOPLE WE KNEW.

She soon found the other students were friendly enough.

HI, I'M JULIE BROWN AND THIS IS MY MATE, MEG.

HI!

HELLO. I'M ANNE HOLDING.

DID YOU SEE THAT DISHY PROFESSOR WHEN WE WERE BEING SHOWN ROUND THE LAB THIS MORNING?

YEAH, HE WAS QUITE SOMETHING, WASN'T HE?

THEY'RE ON DIFFERENT COURSES FROM ME SO WE WON'T EVEN HAVE THAT IN COMMON.

The two boys who also shared the kitchen were doing geology.

...ON FRIDAY HE SAID HE'LL TAKE US ON A CLIMB TO THIS GREAT PLACE WHERE WE CAN GET FANTASTIC ROCK SAMPLES.

MUST REMEMBER TO MEND MY RUCKSACK THEN.

I'LL WAIT TILL THEY'VE FINISHED BEFORE I SIT DOWN. I FEEL KIND OF AWKWARD WITH THEM.

COME ON, I'LL SHOW YOU THESE CLIMBING BOOTS I BOUGHT OFF THIS GUY. OH, HELLO, ANNE.

HI, ANNE. THE SKETCHING GOING ALL RIGHT, IS IT?

ER, YES THANKS, SANDY.

I'M NOT EVEN HAPPY WITH MY WORK. I WAS ALWAYS TOP FOR ART WHEN I WAS AT SCHOOL, BUT HERE THEY'RE ALL SO MUCH BETTER THAN ME.

I JUST CAN'T CONCENTRATE ON THIS DESIGN THEY'VE SET US. I'LL TAKE A COFFEE BREAK THEN HAVE ANOTHER GO AT IT.

THEN HE ASKED JULIE IF SHE'D GOT THE FROG'S LEGS—

AND I LIFTED MY SKIRT AND SAID, 'NO, SIR— I THINK THEY'RE MY OWN'!

THE KITCHEN'S CROWDED, I DON'T THINK I'LL BOTHER...

Another week passed and there was no reply from Mike.

OH, I DON'T KNOW WHAT I'M DOING HERE—IT ALL FEELS LIKE AN AWFUL MISTAKE. I'VE BEEN HERE TWO WEEKS AND THERE'S ONLY BEEN ONE LETTER FROM MIKE. I'VE TRIED RINGING HIM BUT THE LINE'S ALWAYS ENGAGED.

I BET HE'S FOUND SOMEONE ELSE. BUT I'VE GOT TO KNOW FOR SURE. I'M GOING TO WRITE AND ASK HIM OUTRIGHT.

IT WOULDN'T BE SO BAD IF I WAS AT HOME WITH MY FAMILY, BUT SHOPPING FOR ONE IN A STRANGE TOWN MAKES IT EVEN WORSE.

43

I DON'T FIT IN HERE. I CAN'T SHARE THINGS WITH MIKE THE WAY WE USED TO, YET I CAN'T GO HOME EITHER. I'VE NEVER FELT SO ALONE BEFORE. I'M JUST SO MISERABLE.

She tried to avoid the other students.

OH, YOU'RE USING THE COOKER. I'LL COME BACK LATER.

NO, IT'S ALL YOURS, ANNE. I'VE JUST FINISHED MAKING MINE. I CAN'T WAIT TO GET STARTED ON IT—I'M STARVING!

THOSE BEANS DON'T LOOK VERY EXCITING. WHY DON'T YOU SHARE MY RISOTTO. I MADE ENOUGH OR TWO, BUT JIM WENT OUT AT THE LAST MINUTE—

WELL, OK, SANDY. IT DOES SMELL RATHER NICE.

DELICIOUS! YOU'VE GONE TO A LOT OF TROUBLE PREPARING IT. I COULDN'T BE BOTHERED DOING ALL THIS JUST FOR MYSELF.

ME NEITHER. JIM AND I USUALLY TAKE IT IN TURNS TO MAKE THE TEA. YOU SHOULD JOIN UP WITH US, TOO.

So she did.

BEEF CASSEROLE FOR THREE COMING UP.

GREAT!

IF IT'S ANYTHING LIKE THAT CURRY YOU MADE THEN WE'RE IN FOR A TREAT, ANNE.

As time passed Anne began to settle in . . .

I SEE THE FILM SOCIETY ARE SHOWING ' SINGIN' IN THE RAIN ' TOMORROW NIGHT.

I MUST SEE THAT. I'M A SUCKER FOR OLD MUSICAL MOVIES.

WHY NOT COME WITH JIM AND ME?

DOO-BE-DOO-DOO-DOOBY!

WHAT A GREAT SHOW!

IT MAKES ME WANT TO GIVE UP ROCKS AND GO INTO SHOWBIZ!

TONIGHT'S BEEN A GREAT LAUGH, ANNE. WE MUST GO OUT TOGETHER AGAIN—ONLY NEXT TIME HOW ABOUT IT BEING JUST YOU AND ME?

OH, I'D HAVE TO THINK ABOUT THAT, SANDY. I'VE A STEADY BOYFRIEND, Y'SEE.

I'M BEGINNING TO FEEL I'M FITTING IN HERE, NOW. ONE OF THE LECTURERS EVEN LIKED SOME OF MY DESIGNS TODAY AND EVERYONE'S MORE FRIENDLY THAN I THOUGHT. AND I HATE TO ADMIT IT, BUT I'D LIKE TO HAVE SAID YES TO SANDY'S INVITATION.

HAIR

HOW about starting the New Year with a new hairstyle? Here are a few styles to choose from. If you like one, take it along to your hairdresser and ask if they can copy it for you. Or if you live in London or Kilmarnock, pop into one of the top hairstylists yourself!

1 Short Back and Sides?

This style is great for tiny girls. It'll make short necks look long and gives a lot of extra height at the crown of the head. It's a good style for round-faced girls as the swept-back front will give the effect of lengthening your face. It'll give you a "neat" head just right for the latest streamlined fashion look!

Ted Reynell, the artistic director at Sissors, created this look. His tip was that he left the hair full at the sides then pushed the hair up with his fingers, leaving it looking soft and natural.

You'll find a branch of Sissors at 46a Kings Road, Chelsea, London SW3.

2 Disco Cut

Ted Reynell designed this short, spiky look especially for disco lovers. Sissors reckon anything longer would just make the dancer feel hot-headed.

Ted cut the hair to one inch short on top then left it to dry naturally. The great thing is you can freshen it up halfway through the evening by damping it down then running your fingers through it as it's drying.

3 Softly, Softly.

This style by Mane Line, 22 Savile Row, London W1, would be great for someone whose hair is finally growing out from a layered cut. It's a gently-layered bob which has been blow dried into shape.

The fairly-full fringe means that it would suit a long or triangular-shaped face best.

4 Cool Cut

Another Sissor-happy cut which is ideal for summer!

The hair is cut into short layers all over but the layers are left long enough on top to flick softly away from the face.

The shape of the cut is emphasised by the addition of blonde highlights on top and darker layers underneath.

The cut is suitable for most types of hair and can be simply dried by moulding it into shape with the fingers.

WE GO!

5 Soft and Shapely

This perm was created at Jingles using Clynol's Curly Locks to give the hair a light perm. In fact, Clynol's Curly Locks is an extremely versatile perming lotion which can be used to produce soft curls, tight curls, crinkly waves or smooth waves, or anything your hairdresser likes — ask about it.

To achieve the effect in the photo, the hair was cut fairly short at the front and sides but left longer at the back.

6 Long 'n' Curly

This girl's hair was all one length and straight until a stylist at Jingles gave it this curly, bouncy look with a Clynol Uniperm.

There are three branches of Jingles in London — 125 Baker Street W1, 77 Mortimer Street W1, and 125 Wilton Road SW1.

7 Halo, Halo . . .

This angelic, summery look was created by the Steiner styling team. The hair has been permed all round with a Steiner temperate wave and coloured with Steiner Glo-ahead in Ash Blonde.

The crown was blow-dried to keep it smooth and shiny, but the rest of the hair was left to dry naturally to produce a soft halo of curls.

This style would only suit very, very good girls!

And finally, here are a few styles from Kenneth Arthur, a great hairstylist based in Scotland. Our Scots readers will find his salon at 15 Hill Street, Kilmarnock, Ayrshire, Scotland, and other readers might be able to persuade their local hairstylists to adapt the styles for them.
Make-up by Celia Hunter,
photos by Bill Ling and Al MacDonald.

Julie hair, by Kenneth.

Lise hair, by Kenneth.

Linda hair, by Brendan.

47

TO JENNY, WITH LOVE...

A READER'S TRUE EXPERIENCE

IT'S funny, isn't it, how things change? People, too, come to that. Like me, for instance. If anyone had told me a year ago that I, Jim Clarke, would be walking through town today with a bunch of flowers in my hand, flowers for a girl, I'd never have believed it. *No way,* I'd have said . . .

Don't get me wrong — I'd fancied plenty of girls from time to time. But I'd never been what's called the romantic type. Sport was my scene, football, athletics, amateur boxing, the lot. It left me precious little time for dates, or for dreaming about the girlfriend of the moment.

I'd got my life well organised — no ties, no commitments, nothing to hold me back. Till Jenny came along . . .

Jenny was different from all the other girls. It wasn't just that I fancied her — I loved her.

She was little, with dark hair and big brown eyes. The kind of girl who made you feel protective, the kind who could be hurt so easily — I could tell that straight away. And yet I was the one who hurt her — as long as I live that's something I'll never forget.

That's why I'm taking these flowers — to say I'm sorry. Even although I've left it far too late . . .

"She ought to have lived in a different age when blokes were knights in shining armour."

I can picture her now so clearly. She had a kind of *old-fashioned* face, the sort you see in those portraits hanging up in art galleries, and an old-fashioned attitude to match. She ought to have lived in a different age, when blokes were knights in shining armour. But it just so happened that on the day we met, I was wearing a red-striped shirt and the muddiest possible pair of football shorts.

Our first eleven at the Comprehensive had been playing a match against this other school. And we'd won 2-1. I'd felt about 10 feet tall when the whistle blew and we wandered off the pitch. Well, after all, I was the one who'd scored the winning goal . . .

It was then that I'd spotted this dark-haired, dark-eyed girl. She was standing among the straggle of spectators, cheering for all she was worth. She looked at me and smiled, and just for a moment I forgot about the match

These flowers are for Jenny. To tell her I'm sorry, and that I love her. To say I realise how selfish I was. To tell her she was the most wonderful thing that ever happened to me.
But most of all to say I'm sorry that it's too late . . .

and found myself thinking about this girl instead, wondering what class she was in and why I'd never noticed her before.

"I thought you were great," she whispered as I passed her, blushing bright red the moment she'd spoken.

"You're keen on football?" I asked her. It surprised me to find I was blushing a bit myself.

"Yes . . . I mean, no . . ." she stammered, all confused.

That seemed to need a bit of sorting out, so I waited behind and chatted her up for a while. She was quieter than most of the other girls I knew and she didn't tell me much about herself, only that her name was Jenny Forrester and that she'd come new to the school at the start of the summer term.

"They said she was the clinging type, but I didn't care."

It was only later on, when we started going around together, that she told me she'd only come to watch that match because I happened to be playing in it. And from that time on, whatever match I played in, even if it was only a practice one, Jenny was always there.

Of course, my mates were always sending me up about her.

"Watch it," they said, "you can see she's the clinging type — it sticks out a mile."

But I didn't care. She could cling to me as long as she wanted.

Anyway, they'd got it all wrong. Jenny was never possessive or demanding, not like the females other guys went out with. If I wanted to spend an evening with my mates or put in a spot of training, Jenny would be the first to understand. She never nagged or asked me a string of questions. She'd stay at home those nights, washing her hair or painting her nails, or whatever it is girls do when they're on their own. But whenever I wanted her, she was always around.

In other words, I had the best of both worlds, freedom to do whatever I wanted, with no need for excuses or explanations. And Jenny, too . . .

But I had to face it — there was one snag. Jenny was definitely the romantic type, quite different from myself. And it was this that caused the break between us.

It happened a week before her sixteenth birthday. I asked her what she wanted for a present and she looked at me, her eyes all soft and dreamy.

"Look, Jim," she said, "I don't want to *tell* you what I want. A present should always be a surprise."

That didn't make sense to me, and I told her so. I wanted to give her something she really needed, and how was I to know unless she told me? If she'd asked for a handbag or some special kind of perfume, there would've been no problem. As for the shopping bit, I could've safely left that to my sister . . .

Jenny stood smiling at me for a moment. Guessing my thoughts, maybe, the way she so often did.

"Jim, there *is* something I'd like," she said at last. She looked sort of shy and I wondered what was coming.

"I've always wanted you to give me flowers," she said.

Well, I reckoned that was crazy! What was the use of flowers? In no time at all they shrivelled up and died. And it wasn't as if she needed them. Her dad was pretty keen on gardening, and her garden at home was a mass of flowers already — she could gather a bunch of them any time she wanted . . .

Besides, I'd have felt a real twit, choosing a birthday bouquet in a florist's shop, writing some corny, sentimental message on one of those fancy little cards they give you. I wouldn't have had a clue what to put. Oh, no — it just wasn't my scene . . .

"Jenny understood the way I felt — she knew me so well."

I think Jenny understood the way I felt — she knew me pretty well by that time. She looked a bit disappointed for a moment, but at least she didn't go on about it.

The trouble began later — when I broke the news to her that I'd have to be out of town on her birthday.

It was a Saturday and it just so happened that our local football team was playing away. I'd planned to go to the match with my mates, the way I always did — the tickets were bought and our seats on the coach were booked.

I'll never forget her face when I told her. She just looked at me with those big dark eyes of hers, like a kid who'd been suddenly slapped across the face.

"I'll be back in time to take you out," I told her. "It's only a two-hour run — and the disco's open till eleven remember?"

"But — it won't be the same," she said. "You see, I thought . . ."

She didn't go on, but I knew what was on her mind. She'd thought I might put her first, that day of all days.

And just for a moment I almost said I would. But then I began to think about my mates. I'd never have heard the last of it, if it got around that I was opting out because of Jenny.

The match was great — our team was in first-class form and the rest of my gang were over the moon about it. But somehow I found it hard to concentrate. And coming back in the coach, I didn't sing a note or speak a word. In fact, I was hardly aware of the row which was going on around me . . .

I could only think of Jenny. Would she be waiting for me at the bus-stop? Or was she still sore about the way I'd treated her? I could see now just how selfish I'd been. And supposing I'd lost her because of my selfishness?

"I knew she'd be waiting for me. She wasn't the kind to bear a grudge."

I guess it was then that the truth came home to me. I found myself realising just how much I loved her — and how little I deserved her. But I'd make it all up to her. Tomorrow I'd take her out on a really special date. And I'd buy her those flowers — why not? If flowers were what Jenny wanted, she would have them . . .

It seemed an eternity till the bus pulled up. I longed to hold her in my arms again. I'd learnt my lesson. From now on, Jenny would always come first . . .

She was waiting for me, of course. I might have known she would be. Jenny was never the kind to bear a grudge. I saw her right away, as soon as the bus slowed down outside the station. She was standing on the other side of the road, with that dreamy look in her eyes I knew so well . . .

And then she spotted *me*. I saw her whole face light up as she came darting across the road to meet me . . .

There was just no way that lorry could have missed her. Jenny ran straight in front of it, you see. I heard this awful, sickening squeal of brakes. The traffic all came to a halt . . . somewhere a woman was screaming.

Jenny was lying there, so still. And I knew before I reached her that she was dead.

This afternoon I bought those flowers she wanted. Not birthday flowers. The card they gave me to write on was edged in black. I didn't know what to put, so I wrote the first thing that came into my head — *To Jenny, with love* . . . And I meant it with all my heart.

It's too late now, of course. I'll never see her face light up for me again. Yet, somehow, I'm hoping that she'll know how much I love her, and now I don't know how I'll get along without her . . .

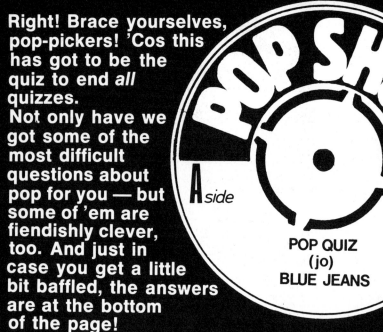

Right! Brace yourselves, pop-pickers! 'Cos this has got to be the quiz to end *all* quizzes.

Not only have we got some of the most difficult questions about pop for you — but some of 'em are fiendishly clever, too. And just in case you get a little bit baffled, the answers are at the bottom of the page!

POP SHOP

A side

45 RPM

POP QUIZ (jo) BLUE JEANS

STARS 'N' STRIPES TEASERS

Name the American groups or singers who had hits with these songs . . .

1. Y.M.C.A.
2. September
3. You Don't Bring Me Flowers
4. Le Freak
5. Givin' Up, Givin' In
6. Always And Forever
7. Just The Way You Are
8. You Make Me Feel
9. My Life
10. Instant Replay

GIVIN' US THE EYE

Mmm . . . just look at these eyes . . . Some of 'em are so delicious you feel just looking at them could melt you down to a little puddle of flesh, bone and throbbing heart!

But who are they?

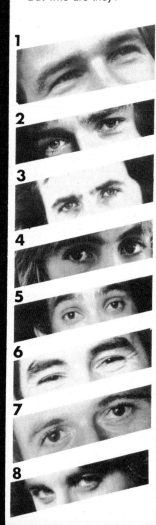

1

2

3

4

5

6

7

8

POP BINGO

And it's eyes down for a full house . . . except this way there's nothing left to chance. All you've gotta do is work out which letters are missing from the titles of the singles given below, then cross out the corresponding letters in the box.

The remaining letters will spell out the name of a group who've brought disco back to where it belongs.

1. L-CK- -UMBER (LENE LOVICH)
2. IN THE N--Y (VILLAGE PEOPLE)
3. -LIVER'S AR-Y (ELVIS COSTELLO)
4. T-AGE-Y (THE BEE GEES)
5. -A-NTER MAN (BONEY M)
6. CHI--ITITA (ABBA)
7. W--AN I- -OVE (THE THREE DEGREES)
8. HEA-T OF -LASS (BLONDIE)
9. BAT O-T OF HE-L (MEAT LOAF)
10. HIT ME -ITH -OUR RHYTHM STICK (IAN DURY)

A	U	Y	T	N	H	D	E	O	G	B
E	E	L	R	G	R	I	E	L	E	Y
U	Q	V	S	N	O	U	M	P	W	M

THANKS FOR THE MEMORY

You're probably sitting doing this quiz huddled up beside the fire in an effort to keep warm, so how's about getting a bit of summer into your life?

Summer means lots of things to different people, but most of us have memories of beach parties, or the jukebox in the café on the esplanade. So see if you can remember the stars who recorded *these* summertime favourites:

1. In The Summertime
2. Summertime Blues
3. Summer Nights
4. On The Beach
5. Surfin' Safari
6. We're All Going On A Summer Holiday
7. Surfin' USA
8. Here Comes The Sun
9. Summer In The City
10. Viva Espana
11. Sunny Afternoon
12. Mr Blue Sky
13. Dreadlock Holiday
14. I Can't Stand The Rain
15. Summer Night City
16. Here Comes Summer
17. Hot Child In The City
18. Summer Breeze
19. Summer Love Sensation
20. Sunny

C	O	U	Q	S	U	T
H	I	C	R	B	L	A
O	H	C	A	R	O	T
T	Y	E	L	A	N	S
C	H	O	L	D	Y	M
L	O	C	O	I	E	N
A	T	E	D	E	B	O

CHECK THIS OUT

"Aargh," you say to yourself, "here's another of these puzzles I just *love* doing!"

But it's all good exercise for the brain, innit?

To solve the puzzle, start at the top-left-hand side of the grid, and by moving vertically or horizontally, find the names of seven groups.

Only one diagonal move is allowed, and that's marked by the arrow.

TAKE ME TO YOUR LEADER

Can you name the lead singers of these groups?

1. Queen
2. Thin Lizzy
3. Smokie
4. Public Image Limited
5. Blondie
6. E.L.O.
7. X-Ray Spex
8. Generation X
9. The Bee Gees
10. Hot Chocolate

FITTIN' THE BILL

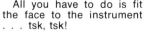

So you still think you know a lot about music? Well, how's about this one, then! All you have to do is fit the face to the instrument . . . tsk, tsk!

C.

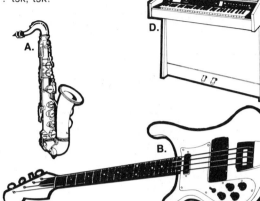

A.

D.

B.

1 PAUL McCARTNEY

3 MIK KAMINSKI

2 LENE LOVICH

4 ELTON JOHN

POP WORD!

Solve the crossword clues to find Blue Jeans' Hunk of '79 . . .

Clues:

1. He might "Pump It Up."
2. He likes a bit of stick — rhythmically if possible.
3. They're gonna "Take On The World."
4. All three of them — in love!
5. They hope the sun might shine.
6. Summer's their time for getting away from "The Sound Of The Suburbs."
7. He "Was Made For Dancing."
8. They'd like us to be "One Nation Under A Groove."

ANSWERS

HANDS OFF!

EVER been at a party where some girl went all out to get off with your fella? What did you do — slap his face, slap her face, or walk out and leave them to it? We asked a few girls how they'd cope — and at the same time we spoke to some guys and asked them what *they'd* do if some other bloke tried chatting up their girls . . .

Camillo Casterina is a twenty-two-year-old barrister's clerk from Fulham.

"I'd just go up and tell the bloke that she was with me and to leave her alone, but I wouldn't make a scene. I might have a moan at my girlfriend if she seemed to be enjoying it, and I might pay her back by chatting up another girl — but it's never happened to me yet.

"I'm not really very possessive, but I think you should stick with the person you go with — otherwise you might as well go on your own."

HANDS OFF — HE'S MINE

Sixteen-year-old Sharon Colby lives in Essex.

"Well, I think I'd be jealous and go and drag my guy away from her — but I wouldn't make a big scene about it. I've done that before, and it just doesn't work. It was a right mess and I ended up sleeping in a car park — so it's just not worth it!

"I'd keep him away from her, if I could — but I'm very lucky, my boyfriend wouldn't leave me out anyway. He always sticks with me at a party — and that's the way it should be. If you want to get off with someone else, then you should go on your own.

"If a boy started chatting me up and I seemed to be enjoying it, then I'd expect my boyfriend to walk away and leave me. Fair's fair, after all!"

Susan Millhouse, twenty, lives in Essex.

"I'd wait till the girl went to the loo — then I'd follow her and corner her and tell her to leave my boyfriend alone. I get very jealous easily, so I'd have a moan at him, too, when I got him on his own outside. And if he really seemed to be enjoying himself, I'd play him at his own game and flirt with another fella, just to show him.

"Mind you, if a boy started chatting me up I wouldn't expect my boyfriend to get annoyed. I'd expect him to look but not mind, 'cos he knows how faithful I really am!"

Sixteen-year-old Leslie Sanders comes from Tooting Bec.

"I wouldn't make a scene. I'd just go up to them, and quietly take my girl away from him. I'm quite possessive really and I get jealous pretty easily, so, if she seemed to be enjoying it, I'd probably have a row with her when I got her on her own.

"I'm the sort who thinks if you go to a party with someone, you ought to stay with them. And it works both ways — I'd expect a girl to walk out on me if I started chatting someone up."

HANDS OFF — SHE'S MINE

HANDS OFF — HE'S MINE

Christine Bruce is nineteen. She's a student and hails from Gwent.

"Well, I think I'd feel very annoyed with the girl, whoever she was — but I'd probably just sit and fume. I'd make sure I stayed on the scene — near to my guy.

"I wouldn't be annoyed with him, well not at first, but if he seemed to be lapping up the attention, then I'd probably walk off and leave him alone."

Sixteen-year-old Jennifer Forsyth is an apprentice hairdresser.

"I think it'd depend on what the girl was like. I mean, if she was really ugly or something then I'd know she hadn't a hope, and it wouldn't bother me. But if she was very pretty or sexy then I'd be over there like a shot. I'd go and ask him if he was coming to dance and take him away as quickly as possible.

"If he fancied her a bit, I'd keep my eye on him for the rest of the party — just to be on the safe side! There's no use just giving up and running to the loo to cry, is there? If you don't fight for your bloke, you don't deserve to keep him, that's what I say!"

HANDS OFF— SHE'S MINE

Nick Brickman is eighteen. He's a stable hand in London.

"I've got implicit faith in my girl — I know she wouldn't take advantage of the situation. I'd be quite happy to let the guy flirt with her, 'cos I know she'd still be faithful to me. I'd never take a girl to a party if I thought she'd go off with anyone else."

Nineteen-year-old Sam Gregory is at college in Liverpool.

"It'd all depend if the bloke was bigger than me! No, seriously, I think it's not the sort of situation you should rush into, screaming, 'Get your hands off her, she's mine!' What good would that do?

"I think I'd just go over and ask my girl if she wanted to dance. That way I could ask her who he was — find out if he was just being friendly, or if he had what they call 'dishonourable intentions!' And I'd also find out whether my girlfriend was enjoying it all!"

HANDS OFF— HE'S MINE

Barbara Robertson is seventeen and comes from Manchester. She's training to be a nurse.

"It's never happened to me yet — touch wood! I suppose it'd all depend on how much my guy was enjoying being chatted up! If he seemed to be lapping up the attention he was getting, then I'd be tempted to go straight over and tell him exactly what I thought of him.

"But if it was obvious the girl was doing all the running and making a definite play for him, then I'd do absolutely nothing. Why should I, after all — she'd be the loser, not me!"

Seventeen-year-old Steve Lewis has this to say.

"It'd depend entirely on what my girl was doing about it. If she was playing it cool and not encouraging him too much, then I don't think I'd do anything. I'd be quite pleased in a way that someone else fancied my girlfriend and that she was mine!

"If she was getting too enthusiastic about him, though, I'd go over and take her away. Subtly, of course — I wouldn't want to cause any trouble. Or if the guy was obviously making a nuisance of himself and annoying her, then I'd go straight over and tell him to leave her alone."

Seventeen - year - old Mary Simpson, wasn't too sure about what she'd do.

"I don't think I'd like it very much, but I'm not sure what I'd do about it. I'd be hurt if he seemed to be enjoying it a lot and if he looked like he fancied her, because then I'd think he was going to pack me in for her.

"I think I'd wait till I could talk to him alone, and I'd ask him what he was going to do. And I'd stick beside him after that so she couldn't get hold of him!"

Robert Green, from London, was pretty positive about what *he* would do!

"Well, I'd feel very annoyed and I'd probably hit the guy who was chatting up my girl! I wouldn't do it in front of everyone, though — I'd get him outside first. And I'd also have a word with my girlfriend, too, if she seemed to be enjoying it.

"I'd probably go and find myself another girl — easy come, easy go, after all!"

HANDS OFF— SHE'S MINE

Peter McInnes is sixteen and hails from Dundee.

"I'd be quite angry and I'd probably go over to the guy and tell him that she's with me, so he'd better lay off. I'd hope that my girl would've already told him that anyway — I'd be very mad if she didn't, and especially if she was flirting with him. I don't think she could mind if I objected to her flirting with other blokes — she's going out with me, isn't she?"

Susan Groves is eighteen. She's a student from Gloucestershire.

"I'd start off feeling very cross — I'd like to smash her face in! If I was with a group of friends I'd sit very quietly till my boyfriend came over, and then I'd say something like, 'Remember me, I'm your girlfriend?'

"I'd probably carry on dancing with other guys who were at the party — and if the girl persisted in trying to get off with him, I'd ask my fella to introduce me to his 'friend.' "

HANDS OFF— HE'S MINE

Brian Stewart is a student from Perthshire. He's nineteen.

"Well, I think lots of people flirt at parties and if I saw a guy chatting my girl up I'd not be too bothered about it — as long as it didn't go too far, of course! I have to admit I've been known to flirt around myself, so I could hardly object to my girl doing it as well!"

The last word goes to Marion Hutchison from Tayside.

"I'd go over and scratch the girl's eyes out! Maybe that's going a bit too far, but I definitely wouldn't like it if some girl tried to chat up my fella. I'd go right over and put my arm around him or something like that — just to let her know he was mine!

"If she kept after him after that I'd tell her to get lost and I'd tell my boy to tell her as well — she'd get the message then, wouldn't she?"

And no doubt she would!

Who's This Guy, Dick Turpin?

You've probably heard that we gentlemen of the road are devils with the ladies . . .

HOW HANDSOME HE IS! HOW STRONG AND RUTHLESS. AND THE WAY HIS EYES GLITTER THROUGH THAT MASK . . . OOH! I'M ALL A- TREMBLE!

But somehow things never quite worked out for me . . .

YOU'RE A DISGRACE TO THE FAMILY, BEN. AN EMBARRASSMENT. USELESS!

I'M SORRY, DAD.

OUR FAMILY HAVE BEEN HIGHWAYMEN FOR GENERATIONS. RESPECTED BY ALL THE GENTLEMEN OF THE ROAD.

BUT NOT ANY MORE. YOU'RE THE MOST INCOMPETENT HIGHWAYMAN IN ENGLAND, SON!

54

57

A ANOREXIA NERVOSA

Better known as the slimmer's disease, it's no joke. Don't become obsessed with your diet, or set yourself a ridiculously low target weight, or it may happen to you. If you need to lose more than a stone in weight see your doctor first.

B BEHAVING

Ask yourself every time you eat something why you're eating it. If it's 'cos you're hungry and you know the food is good for you, go ahead — if it's because you're bored, greedy or unhappy stop, and do something other than eat!

C CALORIES

Calories are the units of energy provided by the food we eat. If you have more than your body needs they turn into nasty spare tyres or bulging bottoms. Foods containing the most calories are fats, proteins next and vegetables least. For example, 1 oz. of cheese contains 120 cals, 1 oz. of chicken 59, and 1 oz. of cucumber 3!

D DIETS

The best diet is a well-balanced one which includes the right amount of foods needed to make your body fit.

E EXERCISE

Eating less food will make you slimmer but you should exercise, too, to firm up your new, slimmer body. Get into the habit of taking some exercise every day; walk to work, have a workout when you get up in the morning or get rid of all your tensions with a good swim.

F FASTING

Some people like to start their diet with a fast as it produces an immediate weight loss and deadens the appetite.

Only fast for about one day a month though, never more often.

G GENEROUS HELPINGS

You can have generous helpings of low-calorie foods like pickled gherkins and onions, boiled cabbage, cauliflower, spinach and bean sprouts, celery, cucumber, marrow, mushrooms, unsweetened rhubarb or any other low-calorie food. Pile your plate high with tasty boiled cabbage. Boil it in stock if you like, eight ounces' worth only contains 24 calories!

A-Z of SLIMMING

H HEALTH

You'll only look good if you're slim *and* healthy. If you cut down on food too drastically you'll look pale and haggard and probably have occasional eating binges, too, which will undo all your good work in minutes. So be sensible and take your time eating a well-balanced diet.

I INVITING

Make your low-calorie meals look

really tasty. Plan ahead. Go shopping for masses of fresh fruit and vegetables then come home and decorate plates with pretty salads.

J JOGGING

Jogging is a good exercise for slimmers who're new to exercising. To begin with just take a ten-minute jog around the block alternating jogging with walking. Then build up the length of time you jog, go at a pace where you can talk to whoever you're running with and not get out of breath.

K KITCHEN

Stay out of it when there's food around.

L LIQUIDS

When you feel like a blow out, swill down a glass of water instead. And when you feel like nibbling, sip delicately from a can of low- calorie fizz. Start the day with a mug of hot water and lemon and always use sweeteners in your tea and coffee. Try drinking lemon tea and black coffee. Cheer yourself up on a cold day with a mug of Bovril, or a stock cube dissolved in hot water, even low-calorie squashes seem more filling mixed with hot water. Before bed, soothe your nerves with a mug of herbal tea.

M MAKE-UP

When you've got a spare evening don't sit in front of the telly, you'll probably end up eating. Go up to your room or bring down a mirror and practise making up your face in different ways. Experiment with hairstyles and use face shaders and shapers to make your face look slimmer.

N NIBBLING

Nibbling is a dieter's major downfall! Nibbles like peanuts, crisps and sweeties may seem very little at the time but they all contain masses of calories. If you must nibble, nibble on low- calorie snacks like chunks of carrot, cucumber or celery or keep a tub of chopped-up apple, lemon juice and raisins handy to nibble on.

O ORANGES

Oranges are lovely to look at and eat. Keep a bowlful in your bedroom. They're only 40 calories each and packed with Vitamin C, which is good for your skin and helps make you feel alert. If you find peeling them a drag, peel one with a knife at home, segment it and take it to school or work wrapped in tin foil. Try segments of orange in salads or heat up two halves under the grill sprinkled with a little cinnamon.

P PACKED LUNCH

Get yourself a couple of plastic sandwich boxes and a Thermos flask or use old cottage cheese cartons and get into the habit of taking a packed lunch to school or work. Forget about sandwiches though. Mix yourself some salads either with fish or cheese mixed in with vegetables or in a separate carton. Put hot Bovril or coffee in your Thermos or in winter pack it with a tasty meat and vegetable stew.

Q QUANTITIES

Fat families often reckon the sign of a good meal is a plate piled high with food! Try to cut down on your normal portions of food and if calorie counting weigh all your food accurately.

Try eating off a smaller plate so that it doesn't look like you're getting a lot less.

R RESTAURANTS

Restaurants rarely cater for slimmers. Remember, a sandwich at home can be low Calorie if made with low-Calorie bread and a little cheese, but in a cafe a cheese sandwich could contain 450 calories So if you're out for a meal, start with grapefruit or fruit juice, then have a grill or fish (no chips!) and maybe a small ice-cream for dessert. Or if the restaurant does children's portions, order one of those in whatever you fancy! Look out for readymeals in the supermarket, many of these have their calorie content marked on the packet, now.

S SUBSTITUTES

The best diet is one where you can eat the same type of foods but can substitute your usual snack or drink for a low-calorie one. For example, spread crispbreads with cottage cheese (40 calories per oz.) instead of Cheddar cheese (120 calories per oz.), nibble on 1 oz. raisins (70 calories) instead of a packet of crisps (145 calories per oz. or toffees, 123 per oz.). Drink low- calorie fizzy cola drink (check the can — some have less than 1 calorie!) instead of ordinary cola (137 calories for an 11 oz. can). Grab an apple (40 calories) instead of a doughnut (253 calories) and try to use sweeteners instead of sugar in tea and coffee.

T TRICKS

Keep these up your sleeve — make rice pudding with skimmed milk and sweeteners, butter toast cold and the fat won't get soaked up so much, buy food which needs cooking or peeling, no easy-to-grab biscuits or sliced bread. Grill food rather than fry it, cook stews a day before and when they're cold skim the hard fat from the top. Fill up on

grilled white fish, 1 oz. contains less than 15 calories.

U UPSETS

Some people go off their food when they're unhappy but most us eat more. Try to be prepared for your off moods, go for a walk, visit a friend or have a bath rather than eat. And if you break your diet one day, don't give up — just resolve to eat a little bit less the following day.

V VEGETABLES

Most vegetables are low in calories — even potatoes, when you consider a baked potato makes a filling meal at the expense of only 150 calories. Revamp some recipes by subsituting vegetables for meat — try a vegetable moussaka, simmer layers of vegetables in a stock cube then top with cottage cheese and brown under the grill or try green peppers stuffed with cheese, onions and mushrooms and baked in the oven.

W WILLPOWER

To keep your willpower you've got to have a very good reason for dieting. Keep some jeans that are too tight handy and keep trying them on!

X EXTRAS

Extras like lumps of butter on your potatoes, a tablespoonful of double cream (82 calories) on your fruit salad, or a wallop of salad cream on your lettuce can destroy your diet. If you must have them include them in your calorie total for the day or substitute.

Y YOGHURT

Yoghurt is as good for you as milk but less fattening if you eat low-fat natural yoghurt (90 per tub). Try it as a sauce on fish and salads. Fruit yoghurt contains more calories (about 150 per tub) but it makes quite a low- calorie sweet. Or mix sweeteners and fresh fruit into natural yoghurts to save calories. Have yoghurt and wheatgerm with fruit for breakfast instead of cereal — it's much better for you!

Z ZZZZ

As usual! If you're slimming you may find you get tired easily so get plenty of sleep. If you're sleeping you can't eat so have a little nap in the afternoon at the weekend if you want. Tell everyone else you're reading! If you can't get to sleep at night because of hunger pangs do a few slow exercises when you get undressed, and, if possible, take a warm bath, then tuck up in bed with a hot drink (preferably not milky) and a boring book to read yourself to sleep. Don't read about food!

GIANT MYSTERY NAME CROSSWORD

This Mystery Name Crossword is just like the ones you see in Blue Jeans every week, only this one is an extra-large, super-sized, bumper crossword including loads of clues about your fave pop, film and TV stars.

All you have to do is solve the crossword clues, then unscramble the letters in the marked squares to find the name of a famous personality.

The solution is printed on page 72 so you can check your answer — but there's to be no peeking if you get stuck 'cos you'll get much more satisfaction if it's all your own work.

Clue to the Mystery Name — A smashing, saintly guy!

CLUES ACROSS

1. A Baker who is Dr Who! (3).
3. John is a Grease-y star! (8).
8. Take a CASE to an INN for dogs, in other words (Anag. 7).
9. Motorists' cinema in the U.S.A. (5-2).
11. Without this, Radio 1 would be silent! (5).
13. Blondie's girl (6).
14. The English/Australian girl of Grease fame (6).
16. When RAIN is about, a country's found (Anag. 4).
17. On film, he had a dragon (4).
18. Anonymous? Do you KNOW, NUN? (Anag. 7).
19. This goes on foot! (4).
21. Scandinavia's top pop group (4).
24. NO CASE is about to reveal large expanses of water (Anag. 6).
26. (And 28 Across) They're "The Professionals" on TV! (6 and 5).
28. See 26 Across.
31. O (7).
32. This Gibb was once Lulu's husband (7).
33. What the Bee Gees are (8).
34. What a bear might give you (3).

CLUES DOWN

1. IN U.S.A. IT is about to become a North-West African country (Anag. 7).
2. Princess Grace lives in this country (6).
3. An elephant's "tooth" (4).
4. Radio 1's Mr Peebles (4).
5. Popeye's girl (5).
6. Do your knees do this when you see your favourite star? (7).
7. A CAMP IS about to show you a prawn dish (Anag. 6).
10. Miss Gordon of "Crossroads" (5).
12. Joanna Lumley was a new one (7).
13. Can you DRAW IN a North Australian town (Anag. 6).
15. It's a capital place! (6).
19. Blue Peter's Mr Groom (5).
20. OUR CART gets upset, leading to a museum's boss! (Anag. 7).
22. Be GLIB NOW about skittles (Anag. 7).
23. The solution to this clue — is the solution! (6).
25. A Buckinghamshire borough — is a snake's discarded skin! (6).
27. Spike Milligan likes to play the ----- on TV (5).
29. Do you like to ---- 3 Across, 26 Across, 28 Across, etc.? (Stare at)? (4).
30. This broadcasting company is for the birds! (4).

ANSWERS

Across — 1 Tom, 3 Travolta, 8 Canines, 9 Drive-in, 11 Music, 13 Debbie, 14 Olivia, 16 Iran, 17 Pete, 18 Unknown, 19 Sock, 21 Abba, 24 Oceans, 26 Martin, 28 Lewis, 31 Nothing, 32 Maurice, 33 Brothers, 34 Hug.
Down — 1 Tunisia, 2 Monaco, 3 Tusk, 4 Andy, 5 Olive, 6 Tremble, 7 Scampi, 10 Noele, 12 Avenger, 13 Darwin, 15 London, 19 Simon, 20 Curator, 22 Bowling, 23 Answer, 25 Slough, 27 Idiot, 29 Ogle, 30 Emu's.

Just looking at this photo of Jean reminds me how close we've always been—until one day . . .

JEAN AND I HAVE ALWAYS BEEN FRIENDS. Y'SEE, WE LIVE NEXT DOOR TO EACH OTHER, SO WE'VE ALWAYS SWOPPED CLOTHES, SHARED SECRETS, AND EVEN GONE FOR HOLIDAYS TOGETHER.

She'll Never Trust Me Again

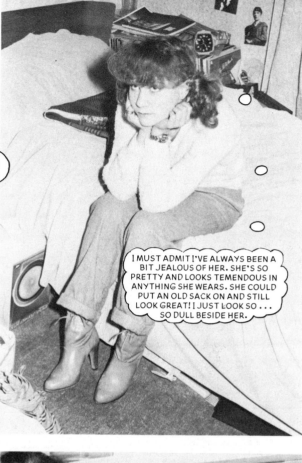

I MUST ADMIT I'VE ALWAYS BEEN A BIT JEALOUS OF HER. SHE'S SO PRETTY AND LOOKS TEMENDOUS IN ANYTHING SHE WEARS. SHE COULD PUT AN OLD SACK ON AND STILL LOOK GREAT! I JUST LOOK SO . . . SO DULL BESIDE HER.

That day she asked me to her party I was feeling kinda low.

ARE YOU STILL OK FOR SATURDAY NIGHT, LUCY? TRY TO COME ROUND EARLY AND YOU CAN HELP ME SORT OUT THE RECORDS AND GET THE FOOD READY.

I CAN'T GO—NOT WITH ALL THESE SPOTS. I LOOK SO AWFUL. I'LL HAVE TO INVENT A HEADACHE OR SOMETHING . . . JEAN JUST WOULDN'T UNDERSTAND.

SHE NEVER GETS SPOTS . . . LUCKY THING. IT'S JUST NOT FAIR—NOTHING EVER GOES RIGHT FOR ME, BUT THINGS ALWAYS TURN OUT FOR JEAN.

So I didn't go, but I couldn't help hearing the music.

IT SOUNDS LIKE A TERRIFIC PARTY. I BET EVERYONE'S HAVING A FANTASTIC TIME. KNOWING MY LUCK IF I HAD A PARTY THE RECORD PLAYER'D BREAK DOWN HALF WAY THROUGH OR HALF THE PEOPLE WOULDN'T TURN UP. BUT THAT KIND OF THING NEVER HAPPENS TO JEAN.

SHE'S EVEN GOT GRAHAM . . . THE BOY I WANTED. SHE'S GOT EVERYTHING!

. . . AND I'VE GOT NOTHING . . . IT'S NOT FAIR . . . IT'S JUST NOT FAIR!

61

BUT, IT'S TRUE, GRAHAM. MAYBE I SHOULDN'T HAVE MENTIONED IT...I'M SORRY...

NO, YOU'RE NOT! YOU'RE DELIGHTED! I CAN SEE IT IN YOUR EYES. YOU'RE LOVING EVERY MINUTE OF IT.

OF ALL THE SPITEFUL, MEAN, CHEAP THINGS TO SAY. I WOULDN'T'VE THOUGHT YOU WERE CAPABLE OF IT, LUCY. IT JUST GOES TO SHOW IT'S TRUE WHAT THEY SAY—YOU LIVE AND LEARN— AND I'VE CERTAINLY LEARNT SOMETHING TODAY.

GRAHAM...I...

AND I THOUGHT YOU WERE SUPPOSED TO BE JEAN'S BEST FRIEND. GOODBYE, LUCY. I HOPE I NEVER HAVE TO SPEAK TO YOU AGAIN!

OH, NO!

HE HATES ME—BUT HE WAS UPSET. MAYBE, WHEN HE'S CALMED DOWN, HE'LL SEE REASON... SEE THAT IT'S JEAN, NOT ME, THAT HE SHOULD BE ANGRY WITH...

But after I'd had a few hours to think about it, things began to look different.

WHAT HAVE I DONE? I'VE BEHAVED LIKE A JEALOUS, SELFISH IDIOT. MAYBE I WAS WRONG...BUT I DID SEE THEM KISSNG...

THERE MIGHT HAVE BEEN A REASON. I SHOULD HAVE CHECKED. SHE LOOKS WORRIED... PERHAPS I SHOULD TELL HER... SEE IF THINGS CAN'T BE STRAIGHTENED OUT.

But, as it happened, it was Jean who told me.

HELLO, JEAN. SOMETHING UP?

IN A WAY, LUCY. I DON'T KNOW WHETHER TO LAUGH OR GET MAD. I THOUGHT I KNEW MY FRIENDS, BUT NOT WELL ENOUGH BY THE LOOK OF IT.

YOU KNOW HOW MUCH I'VE ALWAYS HATED GOSSIP AND PEOPLE TALKING BEHIND YOUR BACK?

Y...YES...I KNOW.

63

WELL, LAST NIGHT, I HAD A BIT OF A FIGHT WITH GRAHAM. IT WAS ALL SO STUPID, REALLY. HE'S BEEN A BIT THOUGHTLESS LATELY AND I FELT HE WAS TAKING ME FOR GRANTED. ANYWAY, I WAS A BIT UPTIGHT WORRYING ABOUT THE PARTY AND EVERYTHING AND I GOT A BIT UPSET AND TOLD HIM A FEW HOME TRUTHS. THEN WE HAD A ROW AND HE LEFT EARLY.

OH, I SEE.

THERE'S MORE THOUGH, LUCY. I WAS ANGRY AND I SUPPOSE I LOST MY TEMPER. TONY BRADY WAS AROUND AND, WELL, I LET HIM KISS ME. IT WAS A STUPID THING TO DO, I KNEW THAT AT ONCE, BUT I DIDN'T THINK THERE WAS ANY HARM DONE.

AT LEAST THERE WOULDN'T'VE BEEN IF SOME 'DEAR FRIEND' HADN'T SEEN US AND TOLD GRAHAM. I'D LIKE TO HAVE A WORD WITH WHOEVER IT WAS, BUT GRAHAM WON'T TELL ME WHO IT WAS.

HE . . . HE WON'T SAY?

NO, BUT WHOEVER IT WAS DID US A FAVOUR. GRAHAM SAYS HE SUDDENLY REALISED THAT HE HAD BEEN TAKING ME FOR GRANTED. NOW WE'RE EVEN CLOSER THAN WE WERE BEFORE AND THINGS ARE BETTER THAN EVER!

MIND YOU, I'D STILL LIKE TO FIND OUT THE PERSON WHO TRIED TO SPLIT US UP. I KEEP GOING THROUGH THE NAMES OF THE GIRLS AT THE PARTY . . . PITY YOU WEREN'T THERE, LUCY, YOU MIGHT'VE BEEN ABLE TO HELP.

YES . . . I MIGHT.

I'D BETTER GO AND GET READY. GRAHAM'LL BE HERE SOON. WE'RE GOING TO THE DISCO TO CELEBRATE GETTING BACK TOGETHER.

HEY, WHY DON'T YOU COME TOO? IT'LL MAKE UP FOR YOU MISSING THE PARTY AND AFTER ALL, YOU ARE MY BEST FRIEND.

WITH YOU AND GRAHAM? OH, . . . I CAN'T. I'D ONLY BE IN THE WAY. BESIDES, I'VE GOT A LOT TO DO TONIGHT.

. . . LIKE WORKING OUT HOW YOU PATCH UP A FRIENDSHIP WHEN ONLY ONE OF YOU KNOWS IT'S BEEN BROKEN.

THE END

HEY, *Lazybones!*

DON'T JUST SIT THERE — EXERCISE SOMETHING!

YOU don't have to be really energetic or sport crazy to exercise. In fact, for most of these isometric exercises you hardly need to move out of your chair. You can firm up and trim down different parts of your body simply by stretching and contracting your muscles.

SLIMMER BOTTOM

BUSTIN' OUT

LOVELY LEGS

WAIST WHITTLER

Lie on your back on the floor with your knees bent up and a book behind your head. Holding the book behind your head with your hands, try to sit up without unbending your legs. Try for a count of six, relax and repeat.

NECKS PLEASE!

You can do this one while you're still in bed. Simply push your head back on the pillow as hard as possible. Push down and hold for six seconds. Turn over and push down with your forehead, hold for six seconds and relax. Repeat both exercises ten to twenty times.

You'll need a fairly strong, four-legged stool or chair for this one. Sit on the floor (c'mon, lazybones, even **we** can manage that!) with your legs stuck out straight in front of you and hook your feet inside the chair legs. Place your hands flat on the floor behind your hips. Breathe in then try to force your feet outwards against the legs of the chair. Hold for a count of six, relax and breathe out. Next, hook your feet against the outside of the chair legs and push inwards for a count of six, then relax. Repeat both parts of the exercise ten times.

TUMMY TRIMMER

Lie flat on the floor on your stomach with your arms by your sides. Keeping your legs in contact with the floor, raise the upper half of your body as high as you can. Hold for six seconds (gasp!), relax and repeat.

Stand up close to the edge of an open door (not the front door or the neighbours'll think you've gone potty!). Bending your arms, place a hand flat on each side of the door with your fingers pointing upwards.

Now, standing up straight, push hard against the door with your palms, as if you were trying to make your hands meet. Hold this pushing position for almost six seconds then relax. Repeat this exercise ten times to begin with, then gradually build up to twenty or thirty times.

Stand comfortably with your arms hanging loosely by your sides and breathe out so your lungs are as empty as possible. Then pull in your bottom as if you're trying to make it touch your tummy. Hold position for six seconds, relax and repeat as often as you can manage. (You can do this exercise anywhere – even at the supermarket or in the bus queue!)

Three Tender Love Stories To Touch Your Heart

THE SCARF

IT wasn't much of a scarf, but it was all she had left — that and the sweet memory of a whole pile of happy days.

He'd picked the scarf for her one day at the market. Green it was, with a brown weave through it. Nothing much, nothing special, but it was all she had.

She kept it close to her whenever she could. To school, around the house, even when her mother smiled. And to bed, where she cuddled it and whispered her own secrets to it.

Even after the one time they'd ever quarrelled and she'd been too filled up with stupid pride to wear it outside, she still held it close at night and buried her face into it, crying.

But then they were together again, and the scarf fluttered about her, proud like a banner of her love, his love, their love.

They'd planned to go to the concert together, to see the man who sang the songs that seemed to be theirs and theirs alone.

December love . . . December love . . .

Promise you'll remember love . . .

They'd planned to go together, saved five-pence pieces in a jar, bought the tickets, planned the journey . . .

After it had happened, she wondered if she could go on her own, if she'd be strong enough.

She made up her mind not to, that she couldn't face it, not without him.

But at the last minute she changed her mind. That even if she was alone, he'd be there. Somewhere. In the music, maybe. Somewhere.

Near the end, when everybody knew the man would soon sing his special song, she found herself on her feet. By the stage.

A PEBBLE IS FOREVER

by Isla Dewar

IT was just a tiny pebble, but green, so green. It lay by the edge of the river just where the water touches the bank and I picked it up, cradling it in my palm.

"What's that you've got?" asked Martin.

"A pebble. It's green and beautiful and I'm going to keep it for ever."

He left his sketching to come over and look.

"It's really something," he said. "We could have it polished and make it into a pendant for you."

"Oh, no. I don't want my stone polished and stuck on a chain. I want it just like this."

Martin smiled, and kissed my nose.

It had been a perfect day, lazing by the river, picnicking. I'd lain in the sun, half snoozing, half watching Martin. He's an artist and I love him. And I never quite know what he's going to do next!

A couple of hours ago, on the way to pick up my watch from the jeweller's, Martin had said, "Let's have a picnic by the river. Let's do it now."

It's always *now* with Martin. 50p was all we could scrape up between us, but it bought a pack of carry-out cheese sannies, one Mars bar and one can of Seven-Up. A feast.

After we'd scoffed it, Martin had gone quiet, taken out his sketch pad and felt-tip pen and started. There was a little creaky old boathouse just across the river from us, which had steps that led right down into the water. Martin was getting it down on paper.

I love Martin when he's sketching. I love him all the time, but when he's sketching it's as if there's just him, the boathouse and his pad, alone in the world. His hand skims over the paper and his eyes flick between his subject and the pad. I like that best. Martin's eyes are beautiful. He has long lashes that curl gently on to his cheeks. Why is it that boys always get things they don't care about — like long lashes?

Eventually I went down to paddle in the river. Icy cold it was! It was then that I discovered my pebble.

"I'm going to take it home," I said, "and put it with my other treasures." My other treasures — memories from other days, other trips, other adventures with Martin. A little blue flower, a gull's feather, precious things like that. I slipped the pebble into my back pocket — to keep it safe.

"C'mon," said Martin, "time we were going. Race you."

We were out of breath and sticky by the time we got back to town. But we still raced all the way down the High Street to the jeweller's to pick up my watch.

That's when I discovered my pebble was missing. It must've fallen out of my pocket during the frantic race, and it quite broke my heart. I sniffed and sobbed, standing there outside the jeweller's shop. Martin gave me a cuddle. The best thing about crying these days is having Martin's shoulder to cry on.

"Look," he whispered, pointing in the shop window, "diamonds. One day I'll be rich, and I'll buy you diamonds by the score."

But I only wanted my plain, unpolished, tiny, ever-so-green pebble.

A lady strutted by, staring at us. She wore super clothes, had perfect hair, polished nails and made me feel awful. I was red-eyed from crying, hot from racing Martin, my hair was sticking all over the place.

"One day I'll be like that," I said, "sophisticated, cool, well groomed."

"Don't you dare," said Martin. So we went home with the miseries, and pebbleless.

But tomorrow was a brand-new day. I came downstairs, and Martin was waiting for me.

" 'Morning," he said, "and surprise, surprise." He handed me a little box, which was lined inside with velvet. Goodness knows how he'd done it, goodness knows how long he'd had to look along the river bank, but snuggled on that plush velvet was my pebble. My tiny green, green pebble.

"A plain, unpolished pebble," Martin said, smiling, "left the way nature made it, just the way you like it. For you, just so long as you stay exactly the way you are now, 'cos that's the way I love you."

And he kissed my nose.

In the cathedral silence, she took the scarf from her neck and kissed it. And threw it softly.

The man caught it, and seemed to sense it wasn't for him, that it wasn't a gift for his vanity, but was beyond that.

He placed it on the piano, sat down, and played. And sang softly.

December   love . . .   December love . . .

Promise you'll remember love . . .

Even when the great hall had emptied and all the people had tipped back their seats and gone out into the night together, arm in arm, cosy, laughing, happy. Even after it all, the girl sat there.

Alone. Beside the streamers and the roses.

Crying softly.

SUNSHINE THROUGH MY SADNESS

by Jo Reade

ME, walking. Lost, lonely and miserable. Just walking.

"You've got to make the best of it," Mum and Dad had said. "It won't be easy at first but you'll soon make new friends. And it is a nice town."

It was a grey town. Too many streets. No familiar faces. No friends. I wished we hadn't had to move here, I wished Dad hadn't taken the promotion. Oh, our house was better than the old one and I had a nice, big room to myself, but I'd never be happy here, away from the places I knew so well, away from my friends.

I turned a corner, walked along another street. And there was the gateway to a small park, just a grassy area with a few trees. I wondered how many more of these little parks there were. This was the second one I'd found that morning.

I followed the path through the trees. A boy was sitting on a bench, reading a magazine. When I saw him my heart sort of turned over. I knew that face! It was fantastic, seeing someone I knew in this town of strangers. But I didn't know his name. I just knew I'd seen him before somewhere.

I didn't know what to say, so I just smiled at him as I passed, hoping he'd remember me. And it seemed that he did, because he said, "Hi. You again."

"Yes," I said, stopping, looking at him. He had lovely brown eyes and his fair hair was sort of curly.

"Not lost, are you?"

"No," I said quickly. Somehow it was important that he shouldn't think I was lost, even if I was. Which I was.

"Oh," he said. "It's just that I saw you coming through here half an hour ago and you looked like a girl who wasn't sure where she was going."

"Through here? This park?" And then I felt my cheeks going all hot. This wasn't the second park I'd been through. It was the same one! And I didn't know the boy at all. I must have seen him on my way through, without really noticing. That's why he looked familiar.

"Yes," he said. "You are lost, aren't you?"

"A bit," I admitted.

"Where you heading for? I'll give you directions how to get there."

"Nowhere," I said. "Just walking, trying to find my way around. Thanks anyway."

I walked on, hoping I didn't look as embarrassed as I felt. Next thing I knew he was walking beside me, his magazine rolled up under his arm.

"New to town?"

"Yes," I said.

"Must be pretty scary, being a stranger. What's your name?"

"Jenny."

"I'm Pete. Want a Coke?"

"I wouldn't mind."

On Saturday mornings I'd meet up with the gang and we'd sit around in Milo's, chatting and drinking Cokes. They'd be there right now, maybe talking about me. I hoped they missed me as much as I missed them. I hoped I'd see them again one day. It made me sad to think about Milo's. There would be nothing as good as that in this town.

Pete took me to a place called "Sam's Caff." It wasn't quite as elegant as Milo's but the music was the same.

"There's usually the same old crowd in here on a Saturday morning," Pete said.

Continued overleaf

**Continued from
previous page**

Two boys came over to our table. "Hi, Pete. Who's your friend?" one of them asked.

"Meet Jenny," he said.

Pretty soon there was quite a crowd sitting around us, boys and girls. Pete introduced me to them all.

"You'll be going to school here, then?" a girl called Sharon said. "Which one?"

"Brightlands."

"Hey, that's my school. Paula and Jane go there, too."

"What's it like?"

They screwed up their faces. "Horrible! No, it's quite nice, really. We'll look out for you on Monday."

Pete finished his Coke and stood up. "Come on," he said to me, "I'm not having this crowd hogging you."

"Where are we going?"

"I'll show you where the Disco is, and the Town Hall clock and all the other exciting spots in town. You gotta be able to find your way around."

We shouted our goodbyes and went off to look at the Disco and the Town Hall clock and all the other exciting spots in town.

And the sun broke through the clouds and suddenly it wasn't a grey and lonely town after all.

"All right," Pete said, later. "You've got the hang of where everything is now?"

"More or less. Thanks, Pete."

He grinned. "So I've finished my duties as a guide. Can you find your way home from here?" He'd done his good deed. Now it was goodbye.

"Yes. I'm sure I can. If I go up there and turn left . . ."

"You've got it. Could you find your way to the Town Hall clock about seven tonight?"

"I could. Why?" But I already knew. And I was glad.

"You wouldn't want to go to the Disco on your own, would you? So why not come with me? I'll be waiting at the Town Hall at seven." Then his grin sort of dropped. "You don't have to if you don't want to. I just thought . . ."

I smiled at him. "I'll be there, Pete. Thanks."

Me, walking. Walking home to my new house in my new town in the sunshine, thinking of new friends and a boy called Pete and not feeling lost or lonely or miserable any more.

*A boyfriend makes you cry
sometimes*

A boyfriend reads your horoscope . . . and makes all the good bits come true.

**A boyfriend is so
many things . . .
best pal . . . worst
enemy. He makes
you happy, he
makes you
sad . . . but, oh,
you love to have
one, 'cos . . .**

A boyfriend holds your hand when you're frightened . . . and also when you're not.

A boyfriend is the reason you drag yourself out on chilly, chilly winter nights t'meet at the Square, and hang around saying what'll we do, where'll we go? Shiver shiver. Only love could bring ya out on a night like this.

A boyfriend says "Bless you" when you sneeze.

A boyfriend writes you soppy letters, and posts them first class.

A boyfriend
*keeps your secrets
secret*

A boyfriend still visits you even though you live on the top floor and all the lifts have broken.

A boyfriend catches your cold just because it's yours.

A boyfriend puts *his* pennies in *your* slot machine.

A boyfriend helps you wind your wool.

A boyfriend lets you win at ludo.

A boyfriend is the only person who can tell you the same joke dozens of times and still make you laugh.

A boyfriend is perfectly capable of borrowing your last couple of quid so's he can pay you into the pictures.

A boyfriend is the chap who loves you so much he lets you warm yer freezing hands under his armpits. Oh, what a gent.

A boyfriend is the person you stand kissing sad goodbyes to at the gate. Then half an hour after you part you phone him up to say goodbye to him, all over again.

A boyfriend is the only person in the world you like (yeah, even *like*) to call you "Tubs."

A BOYFRIEND...

A boyfriend is the one whose face is in your eyes each night before you sleep.

A boyfriend is the only one in the world capable of making you take up your knitting needles to lovingly put together a baggy cardi. Every little plain and purl for him. And you thought you'd left it all behind you in Primary 6 (knitting, that is).

A boyfriend is what it's all about, isn't he? Well, there you are on a Saturday evening, getting all tiddled up, lashing on the mascara an' lippy, hoping secret hopes perhaps you'll meet someone special tonight. Perhaps it'll all happen tonight, little stars shining for you. And it happens, oh you meet him: a new mister in yer life. You drift through the next few weeks sighin' an' swoonin', going all tingly when he says your name. Oh, life's wunnerful. Then. You argue, fight, break up. It's over, how could he have fooled you? He's a pig and a boor. Saturday night it's you again, mascara again, lippy again, hopin' again. Might meet someone special tonight, getting back to the war. Looking at fellas, finding out what a boyfriend is.

A boyfriend writes your name in the sand

A boyfriend is a shoulder to cry on. There when you need him. If the relationship's worth anything at all he ought to be one of your best pals.

A boyfriend is the owner of the last name you secretly put with your first name t'see how they go. Oh, Walter Finglewart — I'm not gettin' friendly with him, no way!

A boyfriend is what keeps ya going through the day 'cos you're gonna see him through the night.

A boyfriend is what makes you suddenly aware of a whole new world. It's full of footy scores and different makes of motorbike.

A boyfriend is often the reason you lose touch with all yer other mates. You see so much of him you quite forget all your other pals. Oh, don't let that happen, 'cos time comes when you might split with him and all your pals will have gone their own ways. You'll find yourself alone and very, very lonely.

A boyfriend is taboo when he's someone else's

A boyfriend lets you know how much he thinks of you. He lets you wash his hair after he's spent months not letting his mum near it.

A boyfriend is the softie who pinches the photo of you bawling yer eyes out at the seaside when you were two and didn't get the candyfloss you fancied, or maybe the sea wasn't so cosy as your bath. Anyway, he an' your mum both look at it and go aaaaah!

A boyfriend is the friend behind the face you study so carefully. Is he happy, is he sad, is he speaking to me nicely today? That face, once strange and exciting and now new, an assemblance of features so familiar and infinitely nicer than any other face in the whole world.

A boyfriend is likely to get mad when you go flirting and showing off in front of other guys. How does he know yer only giving yer little ego a boost?

A boyfriend is all out to replace your old teddy as the cuddliest person of the year. 'Cept he's better . . . he cuddles ya back. An' kisses ya, too.

A boyfriend protects you from creepy-crawlies

A boyfriend makes your favourite triple-decker sandwich.

'SNO WHITE AND THE SEVEN DWARFS

ONCE upon a long time ago when there was no such thing as television, when The Ed was just a boy (yes, *that* long ago) there was a little shop nestling in the hills of a far-off land. This shop was a laundry, run by seven dwarfs — Fonzie, Potsie, Blondie, Bodie, Starsky, Piggy and Fozzie.

All the washing, though, was done by a beautiful girl — sometimes known as the Steeping Beauty — who was called Snow White. Every time she washed something the dwarfs would complain, saying: " 'Sno white enough . . . 'sno white enough . . ." and she would have to do it again. This made her very unhappy, because it left hardly any time for the singing and dancing lessons she was taking.

One day, when the dwarfs were in the back of the shop eating shortbread and mini-rolls and mere trifles, a handsome stranger rode by. Catching sight of the beautiful Snow White, he fell elegantly off his horse and jived over to her.

"I've searched High and Low, Far and Near, Marks and Spencers, for a girl like you." He sighed.

"I've never been in any of those places," she said. "Oi live 'ere."

"Then you must be Oi-live-ere Newton-John," said the stranger, proving just how strange he was. He introduced himself as Prince John of Travolta, a nearby far-off land. "I've had a great idea for a smash-hit musical. But I've been unable to find just the right leading lady until now. I've looked everywhere for someone like you."

"What's the musical about?" asked Snow White Newton-John, intrigued.

"A Mediterranean island," said Prince John. "I'm going to call it Greece. It'll make you a star."

"WHAT'S ALL THIS!?!" demanded Fonzie, Potsie, Blondie, Bodie, Starsky, Piggy and Fozzie, bursting into the shop. "She can't go with you! Who'll do our washing and cooking and washing and cleaning and shopping and washing and slaving and washing and washing?"

"You must let me go," pleaded Snow White. "I'll be famous."

"And we'll be left high and dry," said the dwarfs. "Well, low and dry."

SO Prince John and Snow White talked long into the night, and the dwarfs talked short into the night, and eventually they reached an agreement. If Prince John could make the dwarfs as famous as Snow White they could give up the laundry and she could go and star in his musical. But however would he do that? There was only one chance! He would seek the help of the

Good Witch who lived at the top of a famous far-off mountain! (Notice how everywhere is far-off in these Fairy Tales! How come no-one lives just down the road?)

So Prince John set off on his trusty steed, Greased Lightning. The horse had already appeared in a musical with his master — Saturday Night-Mare — but that's another story.

ALL through the night Prince John rode. On and on he rode. On and on and on and on and . . . well, you get the picture. Through towns and villages he rode. Through the town of crooks and robbers that was so full of low joints it was called Evil Kneeville.

Through the village completely surrounded by meadows full of cows. That's right. Uddersfield.

Stopping once to water his horse (though it never did grow any bigger) and once to speak to a handsome blond singing policeman who tried to thumb a lift (he was a Hutch-hiker) he galloped on and etc. . . .

Until there it was before him, the amazing, astounding, incredible mountain known as . . . Tor Blimey!!

Without hesitation Prince John of Travolta started climbing. It took him twenty yours and forty-eight 'ours. But eventually, risking avalanches and crevices, risking snow slides and tripping over many times, he reached the top! There he met two strange figures, one tall and fat, one short and skinny, both wearing glasses and both sniffling and snuffling with their noses stuck in two hankies because of the cold. He recognised them as the Good Witch's guards, The Two Runnies!

"Next time, come up in the lift," they said.

The two guards led Prince John into a dark cave where, sitting inside a large plastic bag, was the Good Witch.

"Good Witch Styrene," said Prince John.

"Just call me Poly," said the witch. "What brings you here, and if you say your horse I'll throw you out!"

Over the next few hours Prince John explained quickly. ". . . so unless you help me make Fonzie, Potsie, Blondie . . . and all that lot . . . famous, Snow White won't be allowed to star in my smash-hit musical, Greece."

"You're sure you want to call it that?" asked Good Witch Poly Styrene.

"Well, it still needs a little work," admitted Prince John. "But will you help?"

"Easy," said the witch. "I'll invent television, then all your dwarfs can become famous. Of course, there might be some nasty side-effects, like 'Crossroads' and 'Sale Of The Century,' but I'll try and find a cure for them . . ."

So with a PAZZAZZ and a WOOOMF the Good Witch invented TV, and Fonzie, Potsie, Blondie, etc, etc. . . . all got their own shows or went on "Top Of The Pops." Piggy went on to marry a frog, which is known as having Kermitted Suicide.

Snow White and Prince John made their musical, called it Grease, and it slid to top spot in the movie world. A Grease-spot.

And Good Witch Poly Styrene? She got married, too. To a Frenchman called Plastic Bertrand. They had a son called Mac.

And seven grandchildren called Fonzie, Potsie, Blondie, Bodie, Starsky, Piggy and Fozzie . . .

Oh . . . I think that's where we came in . . .

food for thought

Before rushing out to spend pounds on spot lotions, hair conditioners and conceal-all make-up, try this simple beauty-basic... eating!

EATING the right amount of healthy food can do wonders for your skin, hair, teeth, nails and, of course, your figure! And since everyone has to eat some sort of food to live, why not eat food that not only tastes good but does you good, too?

If you eat the following foods every day you won't feel hungry for, or even have time for, nasty nibbles like doughnuts, chocolates or chips. Your basic beauty diet should include three helpings of protein, (a mixture of eggs, fish, cheese or meat is best), a pint of milk, some salad and lightly-cooked green vegetables, fresh fruit and a couple of slices of wholemeal bread spread with a little butter or margarine. But if you want to work wonders on a particular part of your body there are certain foods which are more effective than others.

Super Skin Foods

The skin, which is the body's largest organ, needs plenty of protein and Vitamin A. Both are found in eggs, milk, cheese, liver and kidneys. Vitamin A is also found in margarine, cod liver

oil and dark green vegetables.

Although milk is an ideal skin food, if you are a little plump drink skimmed milk rather than whole milk and save 120 Calories on each pint.

If your skin is greasy and prone to acne and blackheads you'll have to be quite ruthless in your diet and avoid all fried foods, and even fatty foods like chocolate, pork, bacon and sausages. Drink at least six glasses of water a day and start the day with a mug of hot water and lemon juice. Yeast tablets or a couple of teaspoonfuls of dried yeast a day will help clear up your skin as will a helping of bran and wholemeal bread each day.

Dry skin needs more fatty foods than a greasy skin, but again avoid fried foods. Get your fats from whole milk, margarine, egg yolks, cod liver oil, cream and cheese. Lightly-cooked green vegetables, tomatoes and avocado pears will help, too.

Basically all skin types benefit from a diet low in sugar, salt and starch. Avoid highly-seasoned food, food and drinks that are excessively hot or cold and too much strong tea or coffee, too.

IT'S A COVER-UP

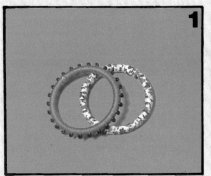

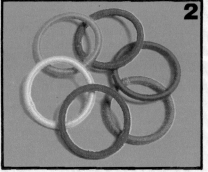

GOT any old bangles you're bored with? Or any nasty cheap ones from when you were a kid that you wouldn't be seen dead or alive in now? Well, here's how to make them into SUPER SMART NEW ones to match your clothes — and cheaply, too!

Just cover them with wool, string, ribbon, or whatever takes your fancy. It couldn't be easier — take a length of wool (the length depends on the thickness of the yarn, but 5 metres of double knitting should do).

Stick one end to the bangle with a tiny piece of sticky tape, and start

Healthy Hair Foods

Hair, like skin, needs protein and Vitamin A for growth but it also needs Vitamin B for health and a good colour.

Vitamin B is available from wholemeal bread, breakfast cereals with added vitamins, (read the side of the packet), milk, yoghurt, cheese (go easy on this if your hair is greasy), meat, (especially liver and kidney), potatoes, yeast and yeast extracts, peanuts and beer.

Iron and iodine are also meant to help your hair's colour. Good sources of iron are liver, meat, green vegetables and eggs, and iodine can be found in spinach and fishy foods.

Sugar and starch do nothing for your hair except give you dandruff so try to steer clear of them. If you have a very sweet tooth eat honey (some say it contains B vitamins) or raisins which have a little iron in them.

Tip-Top Teeth Foods

For strong teeth and bones you need plenty of calcium so be sure to drink your daily pinta. An easy way to pick calcium-rich foods is to look at their colour — a lot of white foods contain this mineral. So go for flour (but pick wholemeal not white), yoghurt, cheese and nuts. Spinach and fish like sardines and pilchards also contain calcium.

Vitamin D is very good for teeth and bones, too. Remember all that cod liver oil spooned in your mouth when you were small? There are nicer ways of getting it, though — cream, Ovaltine and Horlicks, grapenuts, salmon, ox and lamb's liver and good old milk!

Vitamin C is worth a mention here, although it is not specifically for teeth it does go towards building up your body. A daily supply of Vitamin C is essential to good health as it builds up the

body's resistance to infection and keeps your body healthy. Just make sure you have some orange or grapefruit juice every day. You'll find it in green vegetables, potatoes, blackcurrants, lemon and Ribena, too.

Teeth like a good munch — that's what they're there for. So to make your teeth and gums strong eat plenty of crisp carrots, crunchy celery and apples. Avoid eating anything sweet without cleaning your teeth after-wards. Finishing a meal with a piece of cheese helps to clean up your teeth a bit, or swill some water around in your mouth — after you've left the table!

Eyes Bright Foods

Your eyes reflect your general state of health, so even if the rest of you looks great your eyes will betray late nights.

Tired and cloudy-looking eyes are often caused simply by constipation. Avoid this unpleasant condition by eating plenty of wholemeal bread, bran cereals and foods rich in Vitamin B.

If you've dark shadows under your eyes it may mean you're a bit anaemic so eat lots of liver and spinach.

Vitamin A is important for good eye health, but since the body can store this vitamin, go easy on the foods which contain it. After all, just one ounce of carrot supplies your daily requirements and one ounce of liver supplies 3 times the daily requirement. Good eye foods are citrus fruits, dark green vegetables, apricots, egg yolks and fish liver oils.

Generally, if your diet is a good one and you get plenty of sleep, fresh air and exercise, your eyes will look and feel good.

Nice Nail Foods

One thing you definitely should not eat if you want nice nails is your own nails! If you do nibble your nails this sometimes means you are not eating enough calcium-rich foods, so nibble on a lump of cheese instead. You could even nibble egg shells; this may force you to give up the habit altogether.

Nails need foods rich in Vitamins A and D, too. Eggs and fishy foods like sardines and prawns contain both calcium and these vitamins. Fishy foods also contain iodine which improves the circulation, so if your hands are pale and cold try eating fish more often.

If your nails are brittle try taking a little gelatine every day. Just dissolve a couple of teaspoonfuls of gelatine in a little warm water then drink it with fruit juice.

Remember that once you start eating healthily you won't see any results until at least a month, but if you do eat well over that period you'll be looking and feeling so much better than you'll want to eat well for the rest of your life!

winding the wool tightly round and round. Keep it close together so no bits of old bangle show through.

When it's all covered, tie a knot in the end of the wool, then glue the end to the inside of the bangle, pressing it gently in with the wool so it won't stick out.

To show you what can be done, in pic. 1 we've used pink double knitting crepe with beads threaded on at regular intervals, and strips of cotton material.

The bangles in pic. 2 were all covered with Anchor Tapisserie wool.

Pic. 3 has, from the left — string; denim-coloured Wendy Chanson;

purple velvet ribbon; white Patons' Kismet and blue Jaegar chenille spun.

And in pic. 4 we've used gold cotton; pink silk-finish Sellotape; silver Twilley's Goldfingering; blue gift-wrap ribbon and green shiny Sellotape.

We bet you can think of loads more materials you could use, so why not experiment? Have fun!

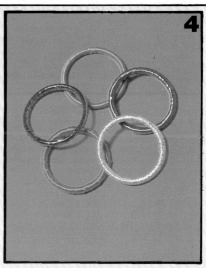

Section I
Dressing To Suit You

1. If your legs are rather short, what sort of boots do you think you should wear?
- a. Ankle boots.
- b. Calf-length cowboy boots.
- c. Thigh-length boots.

2. If your neck was quite long, what sort of tie would suit you best?
- a. A bow tie.
- b. A thin tie with a high knot.
- c. A large wide tie, knotted loosely.
- d. A scarf tied round your neck under the collar of your shirt.

3. If your upper arms are fat and flabby, what sort of top should you wear?
- a. Cap-sleeved T-shirt.
- b. Long-sleeved blouse, with tight, narrow sleeves.
- c. Elbow-length, wide sleeved top with turn-back cuff.
- d. Top with short, puffed sleeves.

4. What style of trousers are the most slimming if you've got big hips?
- a. High-waisted, tight jeans.
- b. Corduroy jeans with zipped pockets.
- c. Baggy trousers worn with a loose blouson.
- d. Jeans and long shirt belted loosely just below the waist.

5. If you wanted to disguise a large bust, would you wear . . .
- a. a short, tight Shetland?
- b. a sleeveless, checked pullover?
- c. a shawl?
- d. a long, loose mohair jumper?

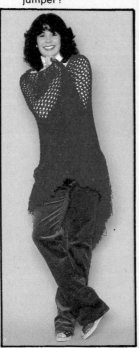

If you're really interested in fashion, you'll probably find these questions easy but even if you don't know what they mean, once you've seen the answers you may have a better idea of what fashion's got to offer you!

Section 2
Fashion Know-How

1. What sort of bag would go best with a flowery, cotton, waisted dress?
- a. Canvas rucksack.
- b. Black patent.
- c. A small, shoulder purse.
- d. Leather briefcase.

2. What looks best with stilettos?
- a. Footless tights.
- b. Short socks.
- c. Patterned tights.
- d. Black, seamed stockings.

3. If you were off to the disco in your new, fine, blue cotton blouse, what colour of bra would you wear?
- a. Black.
- b. Flesh.
- c. White.

4. If you were meeting your boyfriend's parents for the first time, which of these outfits would be the most suitable?
- a. Tight jeans and low-cut T-shirt.
- b. School uniform.
- c. High heels, tight skirt slit up the side and a T-shirt.
- d. Flowery blouse, calf-length skirt and boots.

5. You're going to a dinner dance and wearing a low-necked dress in pale blue. What necklace should you wear?
- a. Wooden beads.
- b. Turquoise stones.
- c. Small necklace in silver.
- d. Black, velvet choker.

JUST YOUR STYLE!

Is fashion your passion? — or are you a walking rag-bag? Try our quiz and find out!

Section 3
Fashionable Words

1. What are French knickers?
a. Parisian panties.
b. Loose-legged knickers — like shorts.
c. Vest and pants all in one.
d. Very tiny bikini pants.

2. What is a bellboy jacket?
a. A jacket covered in bells.
b. A baggy, bell-shaped jacket.
c. A short, fitted jacket that stops at the waist.
d. A military-look jacket.

3. Is a Mandarin collar . . .
a. an orange-coloured collar worn by priests?
b. a polo-neck?
c. a stand-up collar which is open at the front?
d. A frilly ruff?

4. What are espadrilles?
a. Rope-soled sandals
b. Lacy gloves
c. Combs worn by Spanish dancers

5. What is a Sam Browne belt?
a. A cowboy's gunbelt.
b. A belt that goes over your shoulder as well as your waist.
c. Making a dash for the bus when you're late in the morning.

Section 4
Fashion Influences

1. Who made baggy trousers, waistcoats and ties fashionable?
a. Charlie Chaplin.
b. Annie Hall.
c. Bonnie Tyler.
d. Dianne Keaton.

2. Who made walking canes fashionable?
a. Britt Ekland.
b. Charlie Chaplin.
c. Bianca Jagger.
d. Dick Emery.

3. Who made this hairstyle famous?
a. Wendy Craig.
b. Lulu.
c. Marti Caine.
d. Joanna Lumley.

4. Who made this type of cardigan popular?
a. Hutch.
b. Starsky.
c. Marilyn Monroe.
d. Rod Stewart.

5. Who made tight-legged, satin trousers and T-shirts fashionable?
a. Lena Zavaroni.
b. Olivia Newton-John.
c. Shirley Bassey.
d. Princess Anne.

Section 5.
What Have They In Common?

1. What have pegs, loons, bags and bermudas got in common?

2. What have batwings, dolmans and caps got in common?

3. What have cubans, wedges and platforms got in common?

4. What have cummerbunds, sashes and obi's got in common?

5. What have pillbox, panama and boater got in common?

ANSWERS

Section 1.

1. (b) would be best. They'd make your legs look long since they don't fully cover them. Ankle boots would chop your legs up too much.
2. (d) would hide a skinny long neck successfully but if your neck looks OK (c) would do. So one point for either answer.
3. (c) definitely — the other styles would just emphasise your arms.
4. (d) would cover your big hips and look trendy, but (c) would also look good as the loose top would balance out your hips and the loose trousers would skim over them. So 1 point for either answer.
5. (c) would successfully disguise your bust and look good with most clothes. Anything tight would emphasise your bust, as would a sleeveless pullover. A loose mohair jumper wouldn't look too bad but it could make you look top heavy if you're under 5 ft. 5 in. Possible score 5 points.

Section 2.

1. (c) If you said (a) maybe you'd like to be a gipsy.
2. (a) are fun to wear and keep you warm but for dressier occasions (d) would do. 1 point for either answer.
3. (b) If you wore a white bra and there were ultra-violet lights at the disco your bra could dazzle everyone!
4. (d) would probably make them feel happiest about leaving their own alone with you.
5. (c) Turquoises might clash and the other two would look too heavy.
Did you score 5? Possible score 5 points.

Section 3.

1. (b).
2. (c) Although it is a bit military-ish but you only score if you answered (c).
3. (c).
4. (a).
5. (b).
Out of this section there were a possible 5 points to be scored.

Section 4.

1. Score one point for (b) or (d) because Dianne Keaton acted as Annie Hall.
2. (c) Bianca was first with canes but Britt Ekland also carries one, so 2 points for (c) and 1 for (a).
3. (d).
4. Surprisingly (c)! But most people saw Starsky in one first. So 2 points for (c) and one for (b).
5. (b).
You could've scored 7 points in this section.

Section 5.

1. They're all type of trousers.
2. They're all types of sleeves.
3. They're all kinds of heels.
4. They're all worn round the waist.
5. They're all hats.
Possible score 5.

Adding Up Time!
If you scored 20-27 . . .
Fashion is definitely your passion! That doesn't mean you have to work especially hard at looking good, though — your fashion flair comes naturally! Make sure you're always one step ahead in the fashion stakes or you'll end up looking the same as every other fashion fiend in town!

If you scored 13-19 . . .
You know enough about fashion to look reasonably up to the minute, but you're more concerned about what suits you than what's hot from Paris. Few heads'll turn as you walk down the street, but you won't be short of admiring glances from the guys in your crowd.

If you scored less than 12 . . .
You're a real individual! So what does it matter if flared denims aren't in fashion — if you like 'em you'll wear 'em! Your down-to-earth attitude shows in your appearance so you tend to attract like-minded guys 'n' pals. And that's just how you like it, 'cos what matters to you is friends not fashion!

SICK WITH FEAR!

Dad's job in the Air Force kept us on the move, and I seemed to spend most of my time going to new schools. Today was yet another first day, and the reception I got did nothing to still my rising panic.

I thought things were looking up when I met John, but it seemed that my troubles were only just beginning . . .

**A READER'S
TRUE EXPERIENCE**

THERE I was, starting out again, my first day in a new school for the fifth time in my life, and still the butterflies leapt about in my stomach, and my mouth was dry with nervousness as I wondered if this time I'd make friends and settle down. Dad's job in the Air Force kept us on the move, and I hated it. Each time I'd put down roots, it was time to pack up and go. I think Mum realised how bad it was for me, because she kept apologising, and always made an effort to be especially nice to me just before and after each move.

"Have you got everything?" she kept asking that morning, making me check again that there was dinner money in my purse and a gym kit in my bag. I suppose it was her way of asking me if I was all right. She could probably see that I wasn't. I was a mass of nerves, very conscious of my maroon school uniform, a left-over from my last school, that would draw attention to my newness in the midst of all the navy blue which they wore at this school.

But most of all, I was worried about the boys. I'd always been to girls' schools, everywhere we'd travelled. This school, the local comprehensive, was mixed. I'd never had much to do with boys. Our travelling about, I suppose, made me stick closer to home than most girls of my age. And in the married quarters, where we'd always lived, the boys were either younger than me, or a lot older.

The young airmen who filled the camp club every Friday night with drunken singing, then staggered back, still singing along our road, had scared me a bit. Now, with our first real house, on an ordinary estate, my first mixed school, I didn't really know how to behave with the boys I would meet. I felt excited and frightened at the same time.

The journey to school didn't exactly fill me with confidence. As I walked through the estate, great gangs of boys were straggling along, too, kicking stones, or thumping each other, shouting across to friends, whistling and calling after equally-large gangs of girls.

And then I heard the comments I'd been dreading. They all picked out my red uniform. "Look, there's a walking beetroot!" one shouted, and another yelled, "She only needs a green hat to make her look like a traffic light!" I just wished the pavement would miraculously open up and swallow me, so that I wouldn't have to face this for the rest of the day. By the time I reached the school, my face must have matched my uniform.

"It won't be so bad once you get settled down!"

I managed not to cry, and although I could feel the tears pricking at my eyes, the feeling of loneliness was so great that I kept having to swallow back a lump in my throat. Mum had said, "It won't be so bad once you get settled down," and I knew that was true. But already I had an uneasy feeling that settling down here was going to be a lot more difficult than the other times.

I'd been told to report to the secretary's office as soon as I arrived at school. Finding it wasn't too difficult, but pushing through the crowds was. The school was enormous, far bigger than any I'd ever been to.

The secretary seemed flustered and I felt as if I were imposing on her. I stood awkwardly in the office while she scuttled around, trying to find my file. Finally, it was found, and she shouted to a boy who stood outside the door, "Are you a prefect?" The boy nodded. "Look, I'm pushed for time," she said. "Could you show this new girl to room thirty-five? Mr Simpson's class."

"Pleased to!" the boy said, smiling. There was something about his smile that put me at ease for the first time that day. He was the first person I'd seen who made me feel welcome, and I smiled back gratefully, looking at him properly for the first time. He really was very good-looking, with thick, curly, chestnut hair and deep blue eyes. Suddenly I felt embarrassed, awkward again, and my heart gave a little bump and shiver. I liked him.

"Hi. My name's John Betts," he said, guiding me through the maze of crowded corridors. "What's yours?"

"Elizabeth Walters," I said. "Liz, usually."

"OK, Liz. Pleased to meet you. Hope you like it here. It must be a bit strange, though!"

"Oh, it is!" I said. And then I found myself telling him all about our moves, and the girls' schools, and the red uniform. I don't know why I blurted out all my troubles, like that, to someone I'd only just met. It was something to do with the sympathetic tone of his voice, or the gentleness of his blue eyes.

He listened, really listened. Then he said. "Tell you what! You'll be feeling a bit lonely today, before you start making friends. Why don't I meet you at lunchtime, and take you to dinner? Then I could show you round the school. You'll feel a bit more at home when you know where everything is. OK?"

"Great!" I said, almost biting my tongue off afterwards. I'd sounded so eager. But he didn't seem to mind at all. He smiled again, and again my heart skipped a beat. He led me into a classroom, and introduced me to Mr Simpson, a gruff, scowling man who was to be my form teacher. Then he left me, whispering, "Half-past twelve," as he walked past me to the door.

"She's just a show-off!"

It was the thought of his smile that kept me going through that first hard morning. Mr Simpson seemed short-tempered, assembly was over-crowded, I was out of my depth in Maths, and a long way ahead of the class in German. We'd stayed in Germany for two years, and I could speak the language quite well. The other girls and boys in the class smiled at me from time to time, but they were a bit off-hand. One of them, one of the girls, kept staring at me, and I heard her whisper, "Show-off!" when I answered a question in German. I turned bright red, listening to the quiet snigger behind me.

But lunchtime came, and John was waiting for me as we filed out of class. The girl who had sneered at me smiled at him, too, but he had turned away towards me. I saw her glare again, and wondered if I'd stepped on her toes. Perhaps he was her boyfriend. Perhaps that's why she was being so strange. I asked John, "Who's that?"

"Who?" he said.

"The girl with the fair hair, over in that crowd," I replied, pointing her out to him.

He shrugged. "I don't know," he said,

"I've just seen her around."

So I was wrong. The girl must have had some other reason for glaring at me. I tried to put her out of my mind. There'd be more important things to worry about by the end of the day, my Maths homework for a start. Just now I wanted to forget everything and relax.

That was easy enough with John. He looked after me in the dinner queue, kept me laughing through lunch with an endless stream of funny stories about the school, and then showed me round. I was impressed by the size of the school which was even larger than I'd first thought, and so proud to be with this good-looking boy with the carefree manner and easy smile.

"Thanks!" I said, when the bell rang at the end of the lunch break.

"See you!" He laughed, and winked at me.

I didn't know what that meant, but I was disappointed that he hadn't said *when* he would see me again. Still, I thought, that was too much to expect. After all, he'd spent all his lunchtime taking me round, making me feel welcome. The strange excitement I felt when I was with him was my own problem . . .

"Simpson'll go crazy!"

The afternoon got off to a better start than the morning. When I arrived at the classroom there was a little cluster of girls round the fair-haired girl who had glared at me. When they saw me come in, they turned and stopped whispering.

"You're Liz, are you?" the blonde girl said. "I'm Carol!" She sounded as if she was trying to be friendly, although her smile didn't reach her eyes. I smiled at her.

"Yes. I'm Liz," I said. I was glad they were letting me in to their circle.

"Well, listen, Liz. It's Simpson first lesson. History. We have to do these notes in our History books all lesson and I wondered," she paused, "if you've got a fountain pen?"

It seemed a funny thing to ask. I'd never used a fountain pen at school. I'd got one, somewhere in my room at home, but it had lain so long unused that it was probably choked with ink. I shook my head.

"No, why?"

"Oooohh! " Carol said, looking round at all the girls. They looked shocked, that sort of faked shock, and shook their heads.

"Simpson'll go crazy!" Carol said. "He can't stand ballpoint pens. We're not allowed to use them. He might let you off because it's your first day, but . . ." She let her voice tail off, and frowned.

I don't know why I began to tremble. She made it seem so important. And Mr Simpson had been bad-tempered. I'd made a mess of my Maths, I'd been too clever for my own good in German, now it looked as though I was going to be picked on in History. It was too much. The happiness I'd felt through the lunch hour gave way to the panic of the morning. All I wanted to do was to disappear into the crowd, to be like all the rest. I didn't want to do anything wrong.

"Look, love," Carol said, sounding kind and helpful. "You don't want him shouting at you, do you?"

I shook my head, nervously.

"Well, then, I've got a spare pen I can let you borrow for the lesson. I'd like to help you out!"

There was a strange smile on her face, but the kindness of her offer blotted out

Continued on page 81

FROM TOMBOY

Lovely Lesley Ash has come a long way from the skinny, football-playing girl she used to be!

LAST time we had Lesley Ash (this year's annual cover girl), on a Blue Jeans photo session we stopped her from dashing off afterwards to ask her about herself and what it's like being a top model.

Lesley looks so good now I wondered if she was pretty as a child, too.

"Pretty awful, really — compared to my sister, that is! Debbie was the pretty one with cute curls while I was a skinny tomboy with a brace on my teeth! While Debbie played with her dolls I used to play with toy guns or play football in the park with the boys. I've changed a bit now. I mean, I still play football now and then or kick off for a celebrity team but I don't wear my brace any more, thank goodness! I only used to wear it at night but if I had a friend to stay she'd kill herself laughing when she saw me fitting it in."

Lesley as you've seen her in Blue Jeans!

Lesley's mother is Canadian but her dad's British so she's always lived in England.

"I've been over to Canada about three times because my grandmother still lives there but I wouldn't like to live there myself. It seems really dead and it's so big it's as though they can't fill it up!"

SCHOOLING AROUND!

Lesley first went to a convent school but when she was twelve she joined her sister at the Italia Conti, which is a stage school.

"I didn't have any thoughts about going on the stage then, it was just that it was near where we lived in Clapham. My sister had gone there first because she liked dancing and used to go there on Saturday mornings. She made lots of friends so they suggested she went there full time. She told me how great it was there and how you didn't have to wear school uniforms and that you could go out at lunchtime, so after the convent school it sounded fantastic.

"Just before it was time for me to leave the Italia Conti, I thought I'd better find myself an agency because the school wasn't coming up with any work for me, and the one I found told me about an audition for a Levi commercial. I had to audition at the Dance Centre and saw Arlene Phillips, who looks after Hot Gossip now,

and who was casting for it. Luckily, I got the job!

"After I left school I kept on with the agency, but I only got about one active job every six months, so I couldn't rely on that for my living!

"At other times I was working in Jean Machine on Saturdays to earn some cash and one day Jilly Johnson, the model, came in. She gave me the name of a photographer who'd said he'd like to take some shots of me. I recognised his name and I knew he was a good photographer so off I went to his studios!

TO TOP MODEL

"He didn't think I was glamorous enough for the type of shots he took but put me in touch with Freddies, the model agency I work for now. Debbie was already on their books but she'd never suggested I should work there, as I was too young at fifteen. Anyway, Freddie put me on trial and I've had work from teenage magazines ever since!"

COMMERCIAL BREAK!

Lesley and her sister used to live together in a flat but didn't model together because of the four-year age gap. But now it's the other way round. Lesley's got a place of her own but they do fashion shots together now Lesley looks a bit older. Lesley still does quite a few commercials as well as fashion modelling.

"Well, after doing the Levi commercial I became quite well known and did three commercials for the man who does the chocolate flake adverts. We got on well as he said I wasn't spoilt by modelling and was good fun.

"Those adverts led to me going to America and then Greece to do adverts for Harmony Hairspray. At the moment I've done so many commercials in Britain people are sick of seeing my face, so I'd like to get more work abroad if possible. The advert I filmed in Greece for Harmony was for the Austrian market and they seemed to like me there. They even suggested I commute between Britain and Austria to do more commercials for them!"

Lesley's done some film work, too, and you've maybe already seen her in Quadrophenia, a film based on the album the Who brought out about five years ago.

"The first film I did was 'Rosie Dixon Night Nurse.' Debbie was in it and I played a small part as her sister. The film wasn't a success, though, but at least I got some experience by doing it.

"Freddie, my agent, got me the part in Quadrophenia, though. She and her boyfriend were out to dinner with the director and his wife and the director mentioned he hadn't cast the female lead yet. So Freddie said

she'd send him some of her models for the audition, so I went along. I never thought I'd get the part as there were lots of actresses auditioning, too. But after reading in front of the director he asked me to do a screen test. Then I got a phone call to say I'd got the part!"

A NASTY BIT OF WORK!

Quadrophenia is set in 1964, and since Lesley was born in 1960 she couldn't really remember anything about life then. So she had to find out how to do her hair and make-up Sixties' style and how to move and dance as teenagers did then.

"I play a nasty bit of work. I'm a girl who works in a supermarket and first I go out with this fella called Pete, then he drops me, because he's the smoothie and can get any girl he wants. I end up with Jimmy, who loves me and is the main character, but I don't love him, and in the end I get

She's never been camera shy!

the guy I was after all the way through the film!"

Lesley's boyfriend is Rod Stewart's road manager so when she was in the States for the Harmony Hair commercial she joined the tour for four weeks.

"I joined my boyfriend in Denver and carried on the tour with him until Christmas. It was solid touring, but it wasn't boring because we were in a different place every two days. The band are fairly quiet really — they like to have fun but they also work very hard.

"They usually go to the beach during the day to

sunbathe or they go shopping, then they do the gig at night. After the concert they're so full of energy they like to go out for a drink or a meal to calm down, but it's not partying every night or anything. Although when they arrive at a new town the clients usually put on a party for them.

"They usually do two or three gigs in each town, although they stayed six nights in London. When they toured Australia the distance between places was so huge they had to fly to each con-

Lesley in the Boots 17 ad.

Lesley and Phil Daniels in Quadrophenia.

cert otherwise they wouldn't have got there in time!"

A MODEL SINGER

Lesley told us that if she wasn't a model she'd like to be a singer.

"I love singing, so I'd really like to get into it. I've done the odd tape here and there and I did the singing on the Levi's commercial. I don't sing on Quadrophenia, though — it's just the album backing the film all the way through. I've always been interested in singing, because in singing you can really feel the emotions you sing about, whereas in films you're just acting a part.

"I made a single once, but although it got nowhere I'd like to think there's a possibility of doing another one."

Lesley is pretty busy just now doing commercials and some publicity shots for Quadrophenia, so you've probably seen quite a lot of her lately.

"All the publicity could

Lesley in the Levi commercial.

actually ruin me for doing teenage magazines," she explained. "I hope it doesn't, but people get fed up of seeing the same face all the time."

Even if we don't see Lesley on the pages of Blue Jeans so often, we'll be seeing her almost everywhere else. After all, she's done more than a dozen TV commercials!

Not bad for a kid who started out wearing a brace on her teeth!

Materials. — Of Patons Melange 15 (15, 15, 16) 50-g balls in main colour, and 4 (4, 5, 5) 50-g balls in contrasting colour. Keep ball bands for washing and pressing instructions. Pair each 5½ mm and 7 mm knitting needles. Needle sizes quoted are metric; equivalent U.K. sizes are No. 5 for 5½ mm and No. 2 for 7 mm. 2 buttons.

It is essential to work to the stated tension and Patons and Baldwins Limited cannot accept responsibility for the finished product if any other than the recommended Patons yarn is used. Buy the full amount of yarn at one time to avoid variations in dye lots.

Measurements. — To fit 81 (86, 91, 97) cm [*32 (34, 36, 38) inch*] bust. Length 64 (64, 65, 65) cm [*25 (25, 25½, 25½) ins.*] Sleeve seam 47 cm (*18½ ins*) all sizes.

Sizes. — Figures in brackets refer to the larger sizes.

Tension. — 6½ sts and 13 rows = 5 cm (*2 ins*) over garter-st.

Abbreviations. — K — knit; P — purl; st — stitch; sts — stitches; mm — millimetres; cm — centimetres; ins — inches; M — main colour; C — contrasting colour; dec — decrease; beg — beginning; alt — alternate; inc — increase; rep — repeat; sl — slip; p.s.s.o. — pass slipped stitch over; tog — together.

FRONT

Commence at left side edge.

**With 7 mm needles and M, cast on 42 (42, 42, 42) sts.

Work in garter-st. (Every row K.)

Work 10 (12, 14, 16) rows.

Next row. — Cast on 26 (26, 28, 28) sts for armhole, K to end. 68 (68, 70, 70) sts.**

Work 25 (27, 29, 31) rows.

Shape neck.

Dec 1 st at beg of next row, and then on every alt row until 62 (62, 64, 64) sts remain, and then on every 4th row until 60 (60, 62, 62) sts remain.

Work 3 rows.

Next row. — Cast off 15 (15, 15, 15) sts, K to end.

Following row. — K to end, turn and cast on 15 (15, 15, 15) sts.

Work 4 rows.

Inc 1 st at beg of next row, and then on every 4th row until there are 63 (63, 65, 65) sts, and then on every alt row until there are 68 (68, 70, 70) sts.

Work 25 (27, 29, 31) rows.

***Next row.** — Cast off 26 (26, 28, 28) sts, K to end.

Work 9 (11, 13, 15) rows.

Cast off.

BACK

Follow instructions for front from ** to **.

Work 97 (101, 105, 109) rows.

Now follow instructions for front from *** to end.

SLEEVES

With 5½ mm needles and M, cast on 28 (28, 30, 30) sts.

1st row. — P1 (1, 2, 2), K2, *P2, K2, rep from * to the last 1 (1, 2, 2) sts, P1 (1, 2, 2).

2nd row. — K1 (1, 2, 2), P2, *K2, P2, rep from * to the last 1 (1, 2, 2) sts, K1 (1, 2, 2).

Rep 1st and 2nd rows for 10 cm (*4 ins*), ending with 2nd row.

Change to 7 mm needles.

Next row. — (1st and 2nd sizes only).
*K1, K into front and back of next st, rep from * to end.

Next row. — (3rd and 4th sizes only). K2, *K into front and back of next st, K1, rep from * to end. [42 (42, 44, 44) sts.].

Continue in garter-st.

Work 11 (11, 5, 5) rows.

Inc 1 st at each end of the next row, and then on every 16th (16th, 14th, 14th) row until there are 52 (52, 56, 56) sts.

Work 31 (33, 35, 37) rows.

Cast off.

POCKET

With 7 mm needles and C, cast on 60 (64, 68, 72) sts.

Work in garter-st (every row K, 1st row is right side).

Work 21 rows.

Next row. — K7 (9, 11, 13) sts and slip onto st holder, K to end.

Break yarn and slip last 7 (9, 11, 13) sts onto 2nd st holder. Turn.

Rejoin yarn to remaining sts.

1st row. — Sl 1, K1, p.s.s.o., K to the last 2 sts, K2 tog.

Rep 1st row 4 times more.

6th row. — As 1st row.

7th row. — K.

Rep 6th and 7th rows 6 times more.

Work 4 rows straight.

Cast off firmly.

Slip the 7 (9, 11, 13) sts from 2nd st holder on to a 5½ mm needle.

Next row. — K7 (9, 11, 13), and then pick up and K22 sts evenly along left side edge.

Turn and cast off knitwise.

Now, with right side of work facing, pick up and K22 sts evenly down right side edge, and then K across sts on st holder.

Turn and cast off knitwise.

BACK WELT

With 5½ mm needles and M, and with right side of work facing, pick up and K60 (64, 68, 72) sts at lower edge. (1 st for each 2 rows including cast on and cast off.)

1st row. — K1, P2, *K2, P2, rep from * to the last st, K1.

2nd row. — P1, K2, *P2, K2, rep from * to the last st, P1.

Rep 1st and 2nd rows for 10 cm (*4 ins*).

Cast off loosely in rib.

Continued on page 81

BLOUSON BLUES!

EVEN THE BIGGEST OF KNITS COULD MAKE THIS SIMPLE JUMPER

any reservations I might have had.

"Oh, thanks!" I said, grateful for the advice about Mr Simpson, even more grateful for the loan of the pen.

"Think nothing of it!" she said.

Then there was an odd sort of silence, and a suppressed giggle from another girl. I couldn't quite make out what was going on, but I was too worried to question it.

Mr Simpson came into the classroom like a bear with a sore head to take the register, and everyone scattered to their desks. Carol, in the row next to me, was looking straight ahead, smiling a little. The smile frightened me for some reason. I turned her pen over in my hand, wondering if it was some kind of joke that was played on new girls. It might be one of those pens that squirted ink in your face when you took the cap off.

"Fountain pens!" Mr Simpson shouted, suddenly. "History note books!"

"Lay off John Betts. This is just a warning!"

Everyone sprang to attention. He had that sort of voice. I took out my new History note book, and slowly removed the cap from the pen. Nothing happened. I breathed a sigh of relief. I'd been over-suspicious, I supposed, and no felt sorry that I'd misjudged Carol. Smiling, happier, I opened my note book.

Someone had put a little piece of paper inside it, a note written in red ink that glared at me. "Lay off John Betts" it said. "I saw him first. This is just a warning."

I stared at the note, watching the red ink blur before my eyes. Something was going on, something I couldn't make out. Something was going to happen to me, but I couldn't guess what. My hand shook as I glanced down at the fountain pen. Then I dared to look at Carol.

She wasn't looking at me though. She was emptying her bag on the desk and searching through the rubbish.

"Carol Chambers! What on earth are you doing?" Mr Simpson yelled.

"Looking for my pen, sir!" Carol answered, a puzzled frown on her face.

"Forgotten it?" roared Mr Simpson.

"No, sir. Honest, sir. I had it just before lunch. It was in my bag. It's new. My dad bought it for me for Christmas."

"All right! Spare us the details. Has anyone seen a fountain pen walking out of the door? Describe it please, Carol!"

"Red, sir, with a silver cap, and a little silver arrow on the side."

I looked at the pen which trembled in my grasp. Carol had described it perfectly.

"Elizabeth Walters has got a pen like that. In her hand!" one of Carol's friends shouted.

"Elizabeth Walters? Who's that? Oh, you! The new girl! Is that your pen, Elizabeth Walters?"

I shook my head. Now I knew what it was all about. They'd decided to frighten me properly. This was the warning, to be branded as a thief. I felt my eyes fill with tears, knowing there wasn't much I could do about the plan Carol had so carefully worked out.

"That's it, sir. That's my pen. My initials are scratched on the bottom. C.C."

Mr Simpson beckoned impatiently to me. I walked to the front of the class, feeling their eyes on me, wondering if I was going to make it. Mr Simpson glared at me

as I handed him the pen.

"Hmmm!" he growled. "This does seem to be your pen, Carol. See me at the end of the afternoon, er, Elizabeth, is it?"

"Yes, sir," I murmured, trying not to let him see my tears.

I don't know how I managed to get through that afternoon. In every class I sat trembling, trying not to cry, wondering how I'd explain my innocence to Mr Simpson. I'd never convince him. He wasn't the sort of person who'd understand.

When the bell finally rang, it jangled every nerve in my body. Carol leered. The tears ran down my face unchecked.

"Have fun!" she hissed over her shoulder, and giggled as she walked out of the door, surrounded by her sniggering friends. Then the classroom was empty. I was still trying to work out the words to explain what had happened, when Mr Simpson burst in with his usual impatient stride and frown. The moment I'd been dreading. Then he smiled, and I was so surprised that my breath caught in my throat.

"Rough day?" he asked, in a gentle voice, and perched himself on my desk. I wasn't prepared for this. I stared at him, puzzled, and nodded.

"Dry your eyes and tell me all about it!"

"I'm sorry! It can get rough at times, here. It's hard work, just trying to keep up with all the fun and games. We teachers have to be tough!" He laughed. "I'm not really an ogre, you know, and I'm not as stupid as some of them think. I'm just sorry that you had to come in for a Carol Chambers special on your first day here."

I had some difficulty understanding him. But his smile was encouraging. He seemed different, human, not like he'd been in the lesson.

"We've had a bit of trouble with that young lady," he continued. "It looks as if she was trying her tricks on you today. She's been suspected of bullying. Nothing we can put our finger on, but we know there's something going on. Now, wipe your eyes, and blow your nose, and tell me all about it!"

I did, too. He was like my dad, really, all tough on the outside, kind and soft inside. Talking to him was easy, and I told him everything. I even showed him the note.

"Betts, huh?" he asked, raising his eyebrows a little. "Nice boy, that! Now I understand why he's been hanging round outside the classroom door while we've been talking!"

I hadn't noticed. But now I raised my eyes to the door, and saw him peering in, frowning. I smiled through my few remaining tears, and he smiled back.

"Well!" Mr Simpson continued. "I think it's about time I had a serious talk to Carol Chambers. We can't let her frighten my new girls away, can we?"

He smiled again, and put his hand on my shoulder. "I'll see to this, Elizabeth. Don't you worry." Then he glanced towards the door again. "You'd better hurry up, now, and take that boy home, or he'll be late for his tea!"

I shared his laughter, and felt all the panic and anxiety of the day drift away. Mr Simpson would sort things out. Now I could walk home with John, and then try to explain my lateness to Mum. It had been a rough day, as Mr Simpson said.

But tomorrow would be better.

FRONT WELT

Pin pockets to front with cast-on edge matching lower edge and work welt as back, inserting needle into each st on pocket and each alt row on front.

HOOD

With 7 mm needles and M, cast on 99 sts.
Work in garter-st. (1st row is wrong side.)
Work 7 rows.
Break M and join in C.
Work 23 rows.
Continue as follows —
1st row. — K to the last 6 sts, turn.
2nd row. — Sl 1, K to the last 6 sts, turn.
3rd row. — Sl 1, K to the last 12 sts, turn.
4th row. — As 3rd row.
5th row. — Sl 1, K to the last 18 sts, turn.
6th row. — As 5th row.
7th row. — Sl 1, K to end.
Work 1 row.
Next row. — K49 sts, K into front and back of next st, K to end.
Divide for crown.
Next row. — K50 sts, turn leaving remaining sts on spare needle.
Continue on these sts as follows —
Work 1 row.
Dec 1 st at end of next row, and then every alt row until 43 sts remain.
Next row — K2 tog, K to end.
Shape back.
1st row. — Cast off 6 sts, K to the last 2 sts, K2 tog.
2nd row. — K2 tog, K to end.
Rep 1st and 2nd rows twice more.
Cast off remaining sts.
Rejoin yarn to remaining sts.
Work 2 rows.
Dec 1 st at beg of next row, and then every alt row until 43 sts remain.
Next row. — K to the last 2 sts, K2 tog.
Next row. — K2 tog, K to end.
Shape back.
1st row. — Cast off 6 sts, K to the last 2 sts, K2 tog.
2nd row. — K2 tog, K to end.
Rep 1st and 2nd rows once more, and then 1st row once.
Cast off remaining sts.

TAB

With 5½ mm needles and C, cast on 8 sts.
1st row. — K3, P2, K3.
2nd row. — K1, P2, K2, P2, K1.
Rep 1st and 2nd rows once more.
Make buttonhole.
Next row. — K2, sl 1, K1, p.s.s.o., yrn twice, K2 tog, K2.
Next row. — K1, P2, K1, P1 into made sts, P2, K1.
Rep 1st and 2nd rows twice.
Make buttonhole in next 2 rows.
Work 3 rows.
Cast off in patt.

MAKE UP

Press each piece lightly, following instructions on ball band.
Join shoulder and side seams, sewing in edges of pocket at the same time.
Join sleeve seams, leaving 10 (12, 14, 16) rows open from cast-off edge.
Sew sleeves into armholes, sewing the open edges of sleeves to underarms.
Sew cast-off edge of pocket to front.
Join back seam on hood.
Sew hood to neck edge.
Press seams lightly.
Sew buttons at neck and attach tab.

STARDOM

If there's one thing more fascinating than finding out about the people behind hit songs, it's finding out what they were like as kids. *Were* they the same as us . . . especially the girls?

DEBBIE HARRY

"I suppose right from an early age I was a rebel, and I was always outspoken and determined to do what pleased me.

"Not that I was over confident. I always thought of myself as unattractive, although I was dating from the age of twelve so I can't have been too bad. At least I was interested in my appearance enough to start dying my hair very early — usually beginning by bleaching it white and then using all sorts of different crazy colours in dyes you could wash out.

"As for school — I did reasonably well with average sorts of grades in most subjects. But for some reason most of my friends were older than me.

"My musical interests also started young — I was in a church choir when I was eight — and I guess the biggest influence was the radio, which I listened to whenever I was alone.

"Oh, and I had one other 'musical' activity — I was a 'baton twirler,' throwing up the stick in front of a marching band."

TINA CHARLES

"When I was growing up, I seemed to spend a lot of my time coming second in talent contests — usually to some guy balancing spoons on his nose and doing pirouettes!

"I was terrible at school, always getting slapped for day-dreaming about being a singer. And in the end it got so bad I was transferred to a stage school, sort of out of self-defence.

"At that time I only thought about two things — singing and boys. I was so keen to sing like Diana Ross that I used to sit with my ear actually pressed against the record-player speaker to hear everything.

"With boys I had a lot of flings, but nothing serious. There was a boy with a motor scooter and I felt great on the back of that, but really I was only interested in a boy if he was good looking, so every girl could see us in the street and reckon I was lucky to have got him.

"He could be boring, as long as he was handsome. Now, I've changed my mind."

ANNA OF ABBA

"I became involved with music when I was very young by singing with a dance band when I was fourteen. Even before that I used to appear with my father in shows at local theatres, so my growing up was all mixed up with show business.

"Perhaps that's why I'm so eager to stay at home now, and make sure I have lots of time for my family.

"As a teenager, of course, I had boyfriends, but I can't say what sort I preferred. Every boy appealed to me because of a different aspect of his personality. But quite early on I learned to look first at the eyes — the most important attribute we have.

"My favourite sort of dates, when I started going out with boys, was just to walk hand in hand in the woods."

FRIDA OF ABBA

"My childhood was very normal. I was born in Norway but my family moved to Sweden when I was two, so I don't remember much of that country at all.

"When I was a teenager, I loved dancing. I suppose the boys I went out with looked quite like Benny, but most important was whether or not a boy was a good dancer and would take me to a discotheque on Saturday nights."

JULIE COVINGTON

"I was very much a swot, I think. I specialised in science at school, wanted to become a doctor, and finally decided to become a teacher. The only singing I did was in the school choir.

"It was at a teacher-training college that I started to get interested in the theatre — then I got so involved in it that I failed my exams and didn't get my diploma. I never thought I had much talent but there wasn't much choice but to have a try at becoming a professional actress and singer. So I did, and it worked."

MARY TAMM

"I went to grammar school and was very keen on the academic side, so I was pushed to go to university. Then I got accepted at drama school and could break out and do what I wanted.

"Looking back, we were so busy working I can't really say what sort of girl I was. I think I was reasonably popular, I always seemed to be the ringleader when there was any trouble.

"At that age I wasn't really involved in boyfriends at all. I never thought about boys much until I was about sixteen or seventeen and even then it never got serious. I went on the occasional date but never had what you could call a real boyfriend until I was eighteen. A lot of other girls had steady boys and I did feel a bit out of it, but it didn't worry me too much.

"I suppose I didn't really grow up until I left school, came to London to stay with my married sister, and took a job to get my independence."

LENA ZAVARONI

"I'm in the middle of growing up and the fact that I'm sometimes on television doesn't change that. Most of the time I'm at school — a stage school — but we still do ordinary lessons.

"I've got the usual interests — swimming, tennis, going to the cinema. The lady I stay with in London — my parents still live in Scotland — is teaching me to cook and I'm having a lot of fun with that.

"Before I came to London a few years ago everything was very different. I'd been living on a very peaceful island off the Scottish coast and I still get homesick a lot and ring up several times a week. But I couldn't go back to live there now. It's very nice for a little while, for a holiday and to be with my family, but I suppose I have grown up quite a lot while I've been down here and the life there seems to be sort of dead to me now."

OLIVIA NEWTON-JOHN

"When I was at school I wanted desperately to be a vet, but it never happened because I was never very good academically. My method of swotting was to ignore my subject all term, and then swot the night before exams. That was my own stupid way of going on, but of course I never really learned much and I didn't pass many exams.

"I didn't even have pets. My father's a professor and we lived in university grounds where they weren't allowed. But I was a very active member of the R.S.P.C.A. and was always bringing home stray dogs and cats because I couldn't have one of my own.

"I never really expected to become a singer, and even when I first appeared in folk clubs I was always more interested in my current boyfriend and nothing else seemed to matter. I was much more naive and shy then — a bit like Sandy in 'Grease.'

"Even turning professional was an accident. I won a local television talent contest and was offered a contract to appear regularly. There was the big decision to take, about whether to leave school or not, but my teacher suggested I'd never get through my exams anyway, and my boyfriend at the time was also on the show — so I left. Maybe I missed a few outings and dates because of turning professional so early, but not much."

POLY STYRENE OF X-RAY SPEX

"Maybe I'm still growing up — because I still seem to change all the time. But looking back a few years I'm glad it's over. At school, for instance, I didn't do very well, and I didn't like it one bit. The school was supposed to be one of the worst in London but some of the other kids who were there did all right. So it was probably my own fault I didn't do very well. I wanted to learn things through experience not through being told them.

"I really grew up when I left school and started working.

"I spent a while just bumming round the country and needed some money to live on, so I did all sorts of things before I got into music. I was in a fashion shop for a bit — it wasn't glamorous! All I was doing was running round making tea for other people. And I did factory jobs, served behind bars, put on records in a disco — never got near the microphone — worked in offices and even picked mushrooms. I can't count how many jobs I've had, though I always got fed up and left until we formed the band.

"Maybe I'll get fed up with that one day. If I do, then I'll pack it in and do something else."

SUZI QUATRO

"Most of my memories, even early ones, have something to do with music — like hearing my sister screaming when Elvis Presley was on the TV.

"I guess my teenage years were shoved into a very short time — I was on the road playing in a group by fifteen, but I'd gone through the growing-up stages first. I was a tomboy for a long time and boys were pals, until I suddenly started to develop a figure, could wear a bikini, and they began to behave differently towards me.

"My first real boyfriend I couldn't fancy now — he had a crew cut and was a bit chubby — but he was a great dancer and that really turned me on. Our first kiss, though, was a surprise. It was when I was still at the tomboy stage, playing Indians in his back yard. We went into a tent and he just grabbed me. Once I got over the shock, I thought it was quite nice."

Continued on page 88

Skin care

While the rest of your body is usually kept warm and protected by clothing, your poor old face has to brave the elements naked! So you should give your facial skin all the help you can!

Every day and each evening you should cleanse, tone and moisturise your skin. We've worked out some recipes for cleansers, toners and moisturisers to suit different types of skin.

The cleanser you use should cleanse your skin, the toner should close up your pores and freshen your face, and your moisturiser should nourish and protect your skin.

If you look at the skin care feature at the beginning of the annual you'll find out how to recognise the kind of skin you've got, then you can just select those recipes that apply to you!

CLEANSERS

Most of these things sound good enough to eat — but they'll do your skin more good from the outside — honest!

1. Cleansing Grains for Blackheads:
Fill a basin with boiling water (make it 'specially nice by adding some herbs, such as rosemary, thyme, etc.) and lean your face over it with a towel over your head. Hold your face at least ten inches away from the hot water so that the rising steam will open your pores. After about ten minutes, lightly rub a handful of oatmeal over your skin to loosen any blackheads. Rinse off with warm water then splash cold water on your face to close the pores.

2. Cleansing Cream for Dry Skin:
Ingredients: 2 tablespoonfuls vegetable lard
2 tablespoonfuls corn oil
4 tablespoonfuls sunflower oil.
Melt the lard in a pan over a low heat, mix in the oils, stir and leave to cool. Add a few drops of your favourite perfume to make it smell nice.

3. Cleansing Lotion for Spotty Skin:
Add two tablespoonfuls of dried elderflowers to a pint of boiling water in a bowl. Leave for fifteen minutes then strain into a jar or bottle and store in the fridge. Wipe over face with cotton wool night and morning for smooth, spot-free skin.

TONERS

1. Toner for Greasy Skin:
Squeeze the juice of half a lemon into a cup and stir in equal quantities of water and rosewater. Pat gently over face with cotton wool after cleansing.

2. Rosewater and Witch Hazel Toner:
Mix ¾ cupful of rosewater with ½ cupful of witch hazel, or for greasy skin use equal quantities of both.
You can buy rosewater and witch hazel in most chemists.

Moisturising masks

Here're some more lovely ways to feed your face — from the outside!

Avocado Face Pack:
Mash a soft avocado with a little milk or cream to make a paste. Smooth over clean skin and leave for fifteen minutes. Rinse off with cold water.

Banana Skin Softener:
Mash an over-ripe banana with a little yoghurt and honey. If your skin is very dry, add an egg yolk too. Smooth the mixture over your face and leave for fifteen minutes. Rinse off with tepid water. Bananas contain Vitamin A and natural soothing oils.

Bathtime beautifiers

Bathtime is a good time to pamper your body. If you begin now, by the time summer comes your body will be worth showing off in a bikini!

Pre-bath body rubs:
Use one of these before you climb in the tub!

For dull, grey skin — rub a handful of coarse sea salt (available from health food shops) over your body before getting into the bath.

For hot, itchy skin — give your body a rub down with 2 parts water mixed with 1 part cider vinegar.

To soften dry skin and prolong a tan — rub corn or baby oil over your body then stand in a warm place for five minutes before getting into your bath to

WHAT A MIX-UP

Have fun and save money by making some of your own beauty products

allow the oils to soak into your skin.

For sore, dry skin — tie up a cupful of porridge oats in a cotton hankie, dampen slightly then rub the pad over your body.

For pimply skin and a sluggish circulation — rub a loofah over your skin — this helps to remove dead skin.

BATH ADDITIVES

Have a good soak in one of these special baths:

1. Skin softener — add a capful of baby, corn or sun oil, or half a cupful of soda crystals and a few drops of perfume to your bath water.

2. For a soothing soak — steep some rosemary, blackberry or basil leaves in a cupful of boiling water for fifteen minutes, strain and add the liquid to the bath. Even a spoonful of honey added to your water is supposed to ensure a good night's sleep.

3. Bath Salts — You should be able to buy the ingredients in the chemist's. Mix together 2 cupfuls of washing soda with 2 tablespoonfuls of potassium carbonate — add a few drops of colouring and perfume if you like. Store in a jar in the bathroom and use a table-spoonful per bath.

Hair conditioners

Forget all those chemical concoctions and make your hair happy and healthy — naturally!

1. Treatment For Dandruff:
Steep two tablespoonfuls of young nettle leaves (wear gloves when you're picking them!) in ½ pint of boiling water and leave overnight. Strain and add a tablespoonful of cider vinegar. Apply to dry hair, rub in well and allow to dry before brushing hair.

2. Treatment For Greasy Hair:
Steep one tablespoonful of rosemary leaves in a cupful of boiling water for a couple of hours. Strain, add a table-spoonful of cider vinegar or lemon juice and use as a final rinse.

3. Dry Shampoo For Greasy Hair:
Mix together 1 part of Fuller's Earth to 2 parts of talcum powder. Dust into hair, leave for a couple of minutes, then brush out.

4. Treatment For Dry Hair:
Mix 1 part honey to 3 parts olive oil and leave for a day (in the jar — not on your head!). Stir well and apply to damp hair. Leave on for half an hour. Shampoo hair twice then finish with a lemon or vinegar rinse.

Hair dyes

If you feel like changing the colour of your hair do it gently with one of these natural methods.

HAIR LIGHTENERS

1. Stroke some lemon juice through your hair then lie in the sun for subtle streaks.

2. Steep 4 tablespoonfuls of camomile flowers in 1 pint water. After two hours strain and use as a final rinse. Or for a stronger effect mix 1 cupful of the liquid with half a cupful of kaolin (a clay powder available from large chemists) to make a paste. Plaster it on to your hair and leave for half an hour before rinsing off.

3. Rhubarb makes an effective lightner. Simmer 3 sticks of rhubarb, both root and stem, in 2 cupfuls of water for half an hour. Remove from heat. Leave for a further half-hour then strain. Use as a rinse or as a paste by mixing with kaolin, as for camomile mixture.

TO DARKEN HAIR

1. Steep 4 tablespoonfuls of dried sage leaves in 1 pint of boiling water for 2 hours, strain and apply as final rinse.

Continued from page 85

Guess who?!

I'VE HARDLY HAD A CHANCE TO SAY HELLO TO YOU YET! SO HELLO, MY BEAUTIFUL SHARON. HOW'RE YOU DOING?

OH...ALL RIGHT, TOM.

But even this grey cloud will brighten a little as the holiday mood takes over...

AND IT'S UP TO ME TO MAKE SURE IT STAYS THAT WAY ALL DAY TODAY! MMMM...

HEY! BEHAVE YOURSELF, SEXY, OR I'LL DRIVE US ALL INTO A BUSH!

MAYBE I'M JUST BEING SILLY! WHEN TOM LOOKS AT ME SOMETIMES WITH THAT LOVELY SMILE OF HIS I FEEL I'VE GOT NOTHING ON EARTH TO WORRY ABOUT...

But forecasts often work out in ways of their own...

WOW! IS THAT A BIKINI, BARBARA? OR AM I JUST SEEING SPOTS IN FRONT OF MY EYES?

HECK! WHEN SHE GOES FISHING SHE CERTAINLY KNOWS HOW TO BAIT HER HOOK!

AS...ER...CAN BE SEEN THERE WILL BE SOME FLASHING...I MEAN, FLASHES OF...OF...WELL, THINGS WILL DEFINITELY GET A LITTLE WARMER AROUND MID-AFTERNOON! COR!

Although some may still be subject to cold spells around this time...

IT'S HOPELESS! I CAN'T COMPETE WITH THAT! SHE COULD HAVE ANY GUY SHE CHOOSES, AND IF SHE CHOOSES TOM WHAT CAN I DO ABOUT IT?

Very little, it would seem...

COME ON, TOM. I NEED A STRONG FELLA TO HELP CARRY THE FOOD FROM THE CAR, AND YOU'VE JUST VOLUNTEERED!

UH? BUT...OH, OK, BARBARA. I GUESS SOMEONE'S GOT TO DO IT.

HEY, SHARON—WHY ARE YOU TAKING ALL THIS? ANYONE CAN SEE WHAT BARBARA'S UP TO, AND IF YOU DON'T DO SOMETHING SOON YOU MIGHT LOSE THAT GUY. HE'S ONLY HUMAN!

I KNOW, JAN...I KNOW...

And at last a little bit of a storm might break through the heavy, sad skies...

AND WHAT AM I DOING ABOUT IT? JUST SITTING BACK AND LETTING IT HAPPEN! JAN'S RIGHT—I'M A FOOL. I GUESS IT'S TIME I HAD A WORD WITH GRABBER BARBARA...

YOU must forgive me if you find this tale strangely written, for I am not well-practised in the ways of skilful narrative.

And yet, I could not let my account go untold, for it is my earnest wish that it will serve as a warning to those who would seek the powers of evil — and that it will bring salvation to myself.

Papa had forbidden me to visit the Stone Circle. He said it was an evil place. But though his anger made me tremble with fear, I knew I had to disobey him. The power of the stones was too strong to be ignored . . .

THE STONE CIRCLE

A tale of mystery, taken from the strange account of Josephine Thomas.

We had moved to Cornwall in the late autumn of 1873, we being Papa, Mama and myself, an only child brought up to fear the Lord and to respect my parents at all times.

Papa had been an accountant in London for the Deverson Tin Mining Company of Cornwall. Previously he conducted the business from the City, where I had been born, raised and educated, but a change in company policy had resulted in his being called down to Ryekiln, to the bleak and barren surroundings of the dark, secret village that was to bring so much sorrow into my life.

From my first sighting of the town from the coach, as we shouldered the rise above the valley, I was filled with a strange sense of foreboding, and straight away, as if to confirm this feeling, there happened a most upsetting incident. A boy, a ragamuffin little creature, darted across the road in front of our horses and was tossed aside like a leaf in a storm.

He lay moaning in the ditch at the side of the road, a gash on his forehead swelling before our very eyes. At first, I feared Papa was about to fly into one of his rages, but seeing that the boy's injuries were severe, he cradled the urchin's head on his knee and said a few words of prayer.

Then a woman I took to be the boy's mother appeared and she wrapped the limp child in a shawl and scurried off with him, wailing.

It was indeed a most unfortunate affair, and served only to strengthen the feelings of unease I had about the place.

Ryekiln lay in the hollow, and was little more than a scattering of stark, stone dwelling-houses, huddled round the workings of the tin mine.

Veils of mist forever shifted over the roofs, and the chill of the atmosphere seemed to seep into the inhabitants who themselves were surly and cheerless.

In the days that followed, I could scarcely bear to walk through the cobbled streets, for dark depression seemed to seize me whenever I ventured out.

But all this was to change on my first sighting of the Circle.

I CAME across it by chance, while walking on the high ground above the town, in search of something to lift my spirits from the grip of desolation.

The stones were huge, ancient relics of bygone days and ceremonies, and stood in a perfect circle on a shelf of flat land high above the town.

All but one stood on end, like sentinels, silent, save for the restless wind that moved around them. One stone lay flat, and a strange compulsion drew my step towards it.

As I came near, a tingle seemed to stir in my body and flow through me, and I felt as if unseen hands were drawing me close and closer still.

A mixture of dread and longing moved and surged like a sea inside me. I ached to touch the stone, to feel its texture on my hand, to become somehow a part of it, but at the same time, fear froze my trembling fingers above it.

Then, just when I felt I had summoned up sufficient courage to touch the stone, a tremendous roll of thunder rattled across the sky and rain teemed from the black clouds that had gathered all around me.

It was the sudden deluge of rain that broke me from my dreaming. I drew my coat in close about me, and scurried for home.

Poor Mama almost fainted away from the shock when she saw me burst into the hall, a bedraggled figure soaked to the skin.

She fussed over me as she peeled off my clothes in front of the fire.

"You'll have caught a fever, I shouldn't wonder," she wailed. "Look, girl, you're trembling already! If Papa were to know of this . . ."

I could not bring myself to tell her that it was not the fever that had set my whole body quivering. Nor was it the thought that Papa would fly into a rage at the folly of my being out in such a downpour. No, it was the thrill of the stones and their strange power that pulsed through me.

Mama prepared a hot draught and I was packed off to bed, where I fell into a fitful slumber. And then, suddenly, the girl was there.

Her face I could not see, but in movement and manner she seemed a lot like myself in early childhood. Except that her surroundings were those of Ryekiln and not London, and from her costume, I believed her to have been alive several centuries before me . . .

She moved eerily across my dreams, often on the point of turning to face me, but never quite revealing her identity. She was young, perhaps ten, perhaps less.

The figure was swallowed by a mist, and when it cleared, I could see the stones, the Circle. They looked newer and were all standing, although one was at an angle. It was to this stone that the girl was drawn.

IT could have been a dream of my own experience with the Circle, for the girl seemed so attracted to the stones, as I had been. But unlike me, she had no hesitation to touch them, no fear, and she leaned her body close to the stone and spread her arms wide, moving her fingers to touch it and be close.

And in an instant, the sky all around was lit with stabs of lightning, and thunder shook and filled the heavens.

I stirred from the dream for a moment, and lay, breathing hard, in the dark of my room. The world seemed so far away from me, so far away, and moments later, sleep claimed me once more.

And again the girl appeared, but this time, older. And now, as she danced by, she was chased by some young boys who cried, "Evil!" and "Stone witch!" and other names after her. One of the boys bent down to pick up a rock to hurl at her, but at that, she simply turned to face him. For a long moment, she stared hard at the boy with the stone until, suddenly, with a loud crack, it shattered in his hand and splinters of it flew into the boy's face, cutting it and turning it into a mask of crimson.

Choking horror shook me from my dream, and in the wedge of light from my opened door, I saw Mama and Papa standing near me. Papa's fingers clutched tightly to his Bible. I tried to talk but no words came, and when they leaned close to me and spoke, I could hear nothing!

I wanted to shout aloud, to scream, to beg them to help free me from my dreaming, but it was as if a thick glass was between us, and I could do nothing as I felt myself slide away from them, down and down and down into the dark depths of my nightmare.

The girl was older now, perhaps fifteen, and a long dress flowed about her as she walked. She was on some rugged moutainside, and seemed so at one with all around her that I felt myself grow free of all anxiety.

But only for an instant, for suddenly a man was beside her, a huge coarse man with a cruel face and wild eyes. For the shame of me, I thought for a second how like Papa's eyes they were, for when Papa was in a rage, his eyes blazed with the fury of fire, and his whole face took on an almost savage expression.

The man had a flask in his hand, and he was trying to make the girl drink from it. She struggled in vain against his grip, and then, to my horror, he began to claw at her clothing and pushed her to the ground. The girl was screaming and struggling against him, but he was strong, and she could not move for the weight of him.

Her terrible screams echoed loud in my mind. But then, as he broke off to try to swig from his flask, she wriggled free and staggered back from him. The man lay on the ground, laughter crackling from his evil mouth, and as he tried to take more from his flask, the liquid rushed about his face. In his other hand, he clutched a piece of her dress and he taunted her with it, waving it like a flag as he laughed.

The girl stood motionless, staring hard at a point above him. And silently, eerily, a great slab of rock began to slide from the face of the mountain. The man looked up, and fear swelled in his eyes. He opened his mouth to scream, but no

Continued overleaf

sound came, and then he was gone. A hand was all that protruded from beneath the great stone, and for a brief moment, it clawed at the ground, but then a tremor ran through it and the hand became still.

FROM that point on, the girl fled across my dreams, pursued in a terrible chase by hordes of screaming figures. On and on and on she raced in search of freedom, but none was to be found.

And then she was trapped, and hemmed in, she turned and for the first time in all my dreaming, I was able to see her clearly. It was as if I had looked into a glass! Her face was my face, her eyes mine, and the look of fear across them was the same as I felt.

But in that same split second of recognition, a smile came to her pale lips and to her eyes, too. And it was as if she suddenly knew that there was but one place where she could be safe. The light from her eyes seemed to burn right into me, and I found myself rejoicing in the relief she had discovered.

The girl drifted peacefully in my dream until she was in the Circle, and beside the single leaning stone. She turned to me for a moment, her face radiant, her eyes shining, then she faced the stone.

She pressed her body close to it and, silently, it toppled to the ground and claimed her. And yet, there was no terror in the movement, no sense of fear, for all was over in an instant, and I shared with the girl her sweet surrender.

And at that very second, I was free from my dreaming, with Mama and Papa at my bedside.

"Oh, my dear Josephine," sighed Mama, whose eyes were full and red-rimmed. "We feared we had lost you to the fever . . ."

Papa was reading from his Bible. He finished the passage, replaced the marker ribbon in the pages, closed the book and looked up.

"We prayed to the Lord for your return, and He heard us. Blessed is the name of the Lord."

"I — I am well now," I said to reassure them.

Mama touched her hand to my brow, gently stroking my hair.

"We were so afraid for you, my dear," she said softly. "It was as if you were possessed with the fever, and once when you screamed out something about some stones, we thought we were losing you."

"The stones." I smiled weakly. "It's the Circle above the town. I — I know its secret now . . ."

Papa's eyes darkened.

"Such stones are evil, and have no place in Christianity," he said. "It was the Lord we prayed to, and it was the Lord who brought you back to us. You'd do well to think on that . . ."

"But . . . but the girl," I tried to say.

"Let us have no more of this," came Papa's stern voice. "We will have no more talk of these stones, nor will you ever go near them again. I forbid it, Josephine, and you will not go."

Papa's eyes were so dark now, and I feared he was about to explode into a rage.

I closed my eyes, afraid that he might see in them my intentions to deceive him.

I had to go back.

IN the days that followed, my health returned, and my resolve strengthened to go up above the town to see the stones again. More and more, the power of them pulled at me until I knew I could no longer resist it.

Papa, I think, sensed this feeling in me, for one evening in the parlour, he came in from his study with his Bible under his arm. His eyes looked dark, and his whole face bore the clouded look it often had as he brooded. It was a sign Mama and I had grown to fear.

He said nothing as he turned over the pages until he found the reading he sought.

For long moments, his head was bowed over the Book. Neither Mama nor I dared speak, and only the clock and the crackling fire broke the silence in the room.

And then Papa looked up. "Thou shalt have no other gods before Me," he quoted, his voice filling the whole parlour. "No other gods, no stones, no relics of some bygone pagan rites."

I looked to Mama, but her eyes avoided my gaze. There was little we could do but wait until the storm that raged inside him subsided.

But for the first time in my life, it was a storm that did not strike terror all the way through me. For as I closed my eyes, I saw a vision of a rock, and there was no storm in all the world that could do harm to it.

After about a week, and in spite of Papa's stern words, I found myself back near the circle of stones. I knew it was wrong, I knew Papa had forbidden me, but I had a compulsion in me I could not ignore.

My dreaming had troubled me to such an extent that I had to go back to seek some sign that would tell me that what I had seen had been true.

THE STONE CIRCLE

Had there once been a girl who had known the power of stone, and who had suffered because of it until she'd found her peace beneath the stones themselves? And now, were those same stones trying to give of their power to me? The answers could only come from the stones.

The Circle stood waiting.

As before, the fallen stone drew me close, beckoning to me. But this time, there was no feeling of fear inside me. Instead, there was the feeling of joy I had seen in the girl's eyes, and it soared inside me as I neared the stone.

The blood seemed to sing through me and my head spun with all the happiness I held.

I gently placed my fingers upon the stone, and to my complete happiness, it was warm and welcoming to the touch.

"There is no evil," my heart sang. "Here, there is only happiness."

I could feel the strength of the stone pulse through me as I spread my body across it. I was filled with such sweet emotion I felt I could surely hold no more.

And then, suddenly, the roll of thunder filled the air and shook the ground. It was just as it had been in the dream! It was true! It was true! I exalted in the power of the stone!

The great noise rolled on, drumming the whole countryside around me.

And yet the sky was clear!

Below, in the village, the dust rose up from all around the mine workings. And when it cleared, there was nothing. A vast split had appeared in the ground, and all the mine workings had disappeared into it.

In an instant, the sweetness in my body gave way to horror.

When I reached the house, my mother was in the parlour, weeping into the corner of her apron.

"All gone," she cried, as her body shuddered. "Papa, the men, the mine . . . all gone . . ."

Papa's Bible lay open before her, and she began to read from it.

The End.

GOOD NEWS

WE'VE GOT WHEELS TONIGHT!

GREAT!

HARRY'S HADDOCK

BAD NEWS

It's always the way. Something wonderful happens, and there's you floating three inches above the ground, little heart filled with joy and triumph. And then, bang, whump, crash — the bad news, the flattener that brings you back to earth. Oh, it's dreadful — but it doesn't only happen to you . . . These are just some of the things that've had the BJ gang laughing and crying at the same time . . .

THE GOOD NEWS . . .
you've saved enough at last, after denying yourself trips to the pictures and the disco, after scraping all your precious pennies together to go out and buy the hip-huggin' pair of jeans that're gonna drive the fellas wild.

THE BAD NEWS . . .
you've taken so long, so very long to get the cash together — they've sold the only pair they had in your size. Boo hoo.

THE GOOD NEWS . . .
the electrician who's been coming round to rewire next door's house has finally asked you out.

THE BAD NEWS . . .
though he looks super in his overalls, when he's all tidied up for an evening on the town 'e's 'orrible. All punkish and freaky and not your type at all. Oooh, an' he's gonna take you to the disco where you know all yer mates are hanging out at tonight. Groan.

THE GOOD NEWS . . .
the smashing bloke across the disco floor has just come smiling at ya, and asked you to dance with him. And the music's playing real slow. Oooh, your little heart's all aflutter.

THE BAD NEWS . . .
he just wanted to get you alone so's he could ask you all about your best pal, Freda, 'cos he fancies her like mad.
MORE GOOD NEWS . . .
up close, you can see the dandruff on his collar, and his breath smells. Tee hee, lucky old Freda!

THE GOOD NEWS . . .
your little ol' sleepy town has at last got itself a disco.

THE BAD NEWS . . .
it's for over-eighteens only.

THE GOOD NEWS . . .
oooh, swoon, your new fella's finally gettin' round t'kissin' you. T'giving you a huge lovery smackeroni on the lips.

THE BAD NEWS . . .
you've still got a mouthful of chips.

THE GOOD NEWS . . .
your fella phones you up. "Hey," he says, "we got wheels tonight!"

THE BAD NEWS . . .
his wheels are his neighbour's smelly ol' fish van. Dirty grey in colour and "Harry's Haddock" in large letters along the side.

THE GOOD NEWS . . .
your mum an' dad are off for a week's holiday, leaving you at home. Scheme, plan. Hee hee! You'll have parties. Stay up late, keep the lights on, plates of cornflakes at midnight, records blaring and nobody to tell ya t'get to bed, turn the lights off, keep the noise down.

THE BAD NEWS . . .
they're one jump ahead of ya. Aunt Aggie's coming for the week, an' she's heavily into early nights, large plates of semolina pudding, and ancient Mario Lanza records.

THE GOOD NEWS . . .
you finally got round to buying the album you've been fancying for ages. There's a smashing track on it they keep playing on the ol' wireless.

THE BAD NEWS . . .
the track's still smashing. The rest of the LP stinks.

THE GOOD NEWS . . .
your fella says, why not stay at home tonight? Relax, catch the late film on the telly. Great.

THE BAD NEWS . . .
you're stayin' at home — he's off out with Mavis Hillman who has quite stolen his heart away.

THE GOOD NEWS . . .
you met your old feller last night. An' he's still got that smile that used to make your tummy go tingle.

THE BAD NEWS . . .
your tummy still goes tingle, just before you cry.

THE GOOD NEWS . . .
your folks are finally going to get a phone.

THE BAD NEWS . . .
they're also gonna get a padlock for the dial. Wah!

THE GOOD NEWS . . .
your little bruvver finally admits to you that he thinks you're not a bad lad after all. I really like you he says, you're a good friend.

THE BAD NEWS . . .
he's buttering you up. He's gonna touch you for a coupla quid.

THE GOOD NEWS . . .
your fella says you're a tasty cross between Olivia Newton-John and Debbie Harry.

THE BAD NEWS . . .
you're eaten up with jealousy. What's he been doing that makes him feel guilty enough to be that nice to you?!

THE GOOD NEWS . . .
you just got a huge, full-length mirror in your room.

THE BAD NEWS . . .
you just looked in it. Shriek, worry.

THE GOOD NEWS . . .
it'll soon be eight o'clock, soon be time to go meet your fella. Oh, it makes you go all soft and quivery inside.

THE BAD NEWS . . .
if it'll soon be eight o'clock, then it'll be nine then ten and eleven and twelve and you'll have to say goodbye again. Ooh, the pain again.

And now for the bad news . . . it's the end of your BLUE JEANS annual . . . oh, dear, oh, woe, sigh, moan. But what about the good news . . .?
YOU CAN GET BLUE JEANS EVERY WEEK.
DON'T MISS US. WE DON'T WANT TO MISS YOU.

"Hey, who's this? She's never mentioned him before. What's that? He's admiring her dress — doesn't like girls in jeans, he says. Oh-oh — he's got to go!"

"Aah, this one's slightly better. The places he takes us are fun — but the going can get a bit rough! Mind my knee, you clumsy twit!"

"What does she think she's doing? Wearing me for digging the garden! Yesterday it was for washing the car. Could this be the end of a perfect partnership?"

"Ooooh, the disgrace of it! I m a has-been jean! Cast aside for a new pair of jeans! And they're not even as pretty as me! Oh, what's going to become of me?"